Cornerstones of Comprehension

Table of Contents

D1531601

Managing Editor: Deborah T. Kalwat
Editor at Large: Diane Badden
Staff Editors: Becky S. Andrews, Denine T. Carter, Cayce Guiliano, Scott Lyons, Diane F. McGraw
Contributing Writers: Bonnie Baumgras, Jan Brennan, Colleen Dabney, Therese Durhman, Carol Felts, Rusty Fischer, Kim Griswell, Terry Healy, Kathleen Kopp, Kimberly Minafo, Kathleen Scavone
Copy Editors: Sylvan Allen, Karen Brewer Grossman, Karen L. Huffman, Amy Kirtley-Hill, Kristy Parton, Debbie Shoffner
Cover Artists: Nick Greenwood, Clevell Harris
Art Coordinator: Greg D. Rieves
Artists: Pam Crane, Theresa Lewis Goode, Nick Greenwood, Clevell Harris, Ivy L. Koonce, Sheila Krill, Clint Moore, Greg D. Rieves, Rebecca Saunders, Barry Slate, Stuart Smith, Donna K. Teal
Typesetters: Lynette Dickerson, Mark Rainey

President, The Mailbox Book Company™: Joseph C. Bucci
Director of Book Planning and Development: Chris Poindexter
Book Development Managers: Cayce Guiliano, Elizabeth H. Lindsay, Thad McLaurin, Susan Walker
Curriculum Director: Karen P. Shelton
Traffic Manager: Lisa K. Pitts
Librarian: Dorothy C. McKinney
Editorial and Freelance Management: Karen A. Brudnak
Editorial Training: Irving P. Crump
Editorial Assistants: Terrie Head, Hope Rodgers, Jan E. Witcher

www.themailbox.com

©2003 by THE EDUCATION CENTER, INC.
All rights reserved.
ISBN #1-56234-534-6

Manufactured in the United States
10 9 8 7 6 5 4 3 2 1

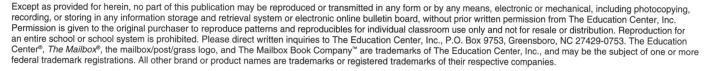

Cornerstones of Comprehension grade 5

Research reveals that the single most valuable activity for developing students' comprehension is reading itself. At its core, comprehension is an active process in which readers think about text and gain meaning from it. In order for students to build competence in comprehension, their reading should be purposeful and reflective. *Cornerstones of Comprehension* is a resource that provides the instructional framework to help your students build essential comprehension skills and achieve success in reading!

Comprehension Basics

Comprehension begins with what a student knows about a topic. It builds as a child reads and actively makes connections between new information and prior knowledge. Understanding is increased as the student organizes what he has read in relationship to what he already knows. To successfully comprehend, students need to master a variety of critical skills, such as constructing word meanings from context, predicting, determining main ideas and locating details to support them, sequencing, drawing conclusions, summarizing, and sensing an author's purpose. *Cornerstones of Comprehension* provides multiple opportunities for reinforcing these essential skills, resulting in increased learning and competence in reading.

About This Book

Eighteen high-interest reading selections, each accompanied by five activities and two to three reproducible skill sheets, are featured in this book. (See the unit features detailed below.) Each unit is clearly organized and highlights one of the following topics: sports, famous people, animals, oddities, real-life mysteries, and adventure. *Cornerstones of Comprehension* will help you help your students strengthen comprehension and achieve reading success, while promoting reading for enjoyment and information.

• Reading Selection

The grade-specific nonfiction reading selections may be used as read-alouds, for partner reading, or for independent reading. Each original fact-based selection was carefully crafted to reflect the interests and abilities of your fifth graders. Content-area text is written in a narrative style and contains eight to 12 highlighted key vocabulary words. All selections are reproducible.

• Skill-Based Activities

Five skill-based activities for use before, during, and after reading accompany each selection. Grade-appropriate skills within activities are clearly identified and explained. Critical skills are featured throughout the units, providing multiple opportunities to reinforce learning and build reading competence.

• Skill Sheets

Each unit includes two or three reproducible skill sheets tied to the reading selection and selected activities. Use these skill sheets to provide further practice with skills, or for informal assessment of comprehension skills.

The King of Swing

Mark McGwire wasn't too **picky** about which sport he played as a boy. As one of five brothers, he spent time tossing baseballs, hitting golf balls, and kicking soccer balls. He was a big kid with red hair, taller and stronger than most boys his age. His friends called him Tree. His size reminded them of the giant **redwoods** north of their hometown of Claremont, California.

Mark joined his first baseball league when he was eight years old. The goal of the **league** was to teach young players how to throw and catch the ball and how to **swing** the bat. Mark learned to throw the ball fast. He also learned to hit far. Before long, Mark started playing Little League Baseball. The first time he was up to bat, he blasted the ball, sending it **sailing** over the fence for a home run. What an exciting moment that was! Mark liked playing baseball!

Mark probably wasn't the coolest kid around. He was shy. Kids played jokes on him because he was easily frightened. Once, during a Little League game, he **pitched** so badly that he finally started to cry. Not cool! After the game, he told his father that things looked fuzzy from a distance. A visit to the eye doctor and a new pair of glasses were all he needed to get back into the swing of things.

Mark worked hard on swinging the bat and pitching the ball. He had a natural athletic **talent.** Mark pitched for his high school team. He had good control and could hurl the ball nearly 90 miles per hour. He didn't get the chance to play much because the coach didn't want Mark to be injured. When Mark did get to hit, his **performance** was impressive. At one game, Mark hit the ball over a 320-foot fence. At another field, he sent the ball flying over a fence and across the street, where it landed in the next county.

After high school, Mark was **recruited** by the University of Southern California. The coach thought Mark had the **potential** to be great at both pitching and hitting. His first year of college ball was tough. At the end of the year, Mark went to Alaska to play summer ball. He missed his family and wanted to go home, but his coach wouldn't let him. He thought that Mark could be an outstanding hitter and wanted him to play first base instead of pitching. Stuck 2,500 miles from home, Mark decided to listen to his coach. He was a hard worker and spent hours practicing in a **batting cage** near the ball field.

Mark got plenty of coaching during his time in Alaska. At first, he gripped the bat too tightly. He had a long, loopy swing. He learned to recognize pitches. His swing got quicker and longer. When he went back to USC, he wanted to stop pitching and become a hitter instead. By his second year he had taken over at first base and was hitting full time. Before he left USC, he smashed home run records set years before.

By the time Mark grabbed the bat for the St. Louis Cardinals in 1998, he was well on his way to becoming the king of swing. First, he had to beat the record of 61 homers in a season. Forty thousand fans screamed as he stepped up to the plate after his 61st homer. Despite the **pressure,** Mark blasted his 62nd homer. He had smashed the earlier record with the crack of a bat. He finished the season with 70 homers to his credit. The boy known as Tree had turned into Big Mac. He'd taken his own special swing and worked hard to turn himself into a star home run hitter.

The King of Swing
Activities

1 Vocabulary

Challenge students to join the League of Vocabulary Champions with this activity! Before reading the selection, divide the class into four groups. Give each group a marker and a sheet of chart paper to label as shown. Assign two groups the first six boldfaced words and two groups the remaining six boldfaced words. Have groups record the words on the first column of their charts and then complete the second column to tell what they know or predict about

Vocabulary Word	What I Know or Predict	What I Learned
1. picky	choosy trees	
2. redwoods		
3. league		
4. swing		
5. sailing		
6. pitched		

each word's meaning. After reading the selection, have each group complete the last column. Combine the four groups into two so that each new group can have a complete set of words. Have each group cover its last columns and then take turns guessing the meanings of its words. For each correct definition, have the group draw a baseball on the chart. The group with more baseballs wins!

2 Fact and Opinion

Warm up fact-and-opinion skills with this activity. After each student reads the selection, have him write one fact and one opinion about Mark McGwire on his paper. In turn, have a student read aloud one of his sentences. Then let him call on a classmate to identify the statement as a fact or an opinion. If correct, let the classmate read one of his statements next. For further practice, have each student complete the activity on page 5 as directed.

3 Sequence of Events

For a winning sequence activity, give each student a copy of page 6, along with a pair of scissors and clear tape. Then have students complete the page as directed. As an extension, discuss with students how Mark's future might have been different if he had continued to pitch. What changes might there have been in the order of events on the sequence strips the students completed?

4 Character Traits

Examine the traits that characterize Mark McGwire with this activity. Have each student label a large, white circle cutout as shown. Direct her to fill the first column with traits that characterize McGwire according to the selection. In the third column, have the student list traits that describe herself. In the middle column, have her list similarities between her and McGwire. Post the baseballs on a bulletin board titled "Mark and Me."

5 Imagery

"The King of Swing" uses imagery to help the reader see Mark McGwire and his baseball heroics in action. Remind students that *imagery* includes descriptions that express ideas in a vivid way, making stories and poems more interesting to read. Then give each student a copy of page 7. After reading the introduction and directions, have each student complete the page as directed.

Is That a Fact?

Take a close look at "The King of Swing," and you'll find both facts and opinions. Can you tell the difference between the two?

Part 1: Below are several statements about Mark McGwire.

If the statement is a fact, change the circle into a baseball.

If the statement is an opinion, change the circle into a baseball cap.

1. Mark spent time tossing baseballs, hitting golf balls, and kicking soccer balls.

2. Mark's friends called him Tree.

3. It was exciting when Mark hit his first home run.

4. Mark had poor eyesight and needed glasses.

5. It seems as though Mark liked playing baseball.

6. Being shy must have been a problem for Mark.

7. Mark was recruited by the University of Southern California.

8. Mark wasn't the coolest kid around.

9. Mark went to Alaska after his first year at USC.

10. Mark probably felt nervous as he stepped up to hit the 62nd home run.

11. Mark hit his 62nd homer.

12. Mark finished the season with 70 homers.

Part 2: On the back of this sheet, write an opinion that each person listed below might have today about Mark McGwire.

1. Mark's father or mother

2. One of Mark's friends

3. Mark's college coach

4. One of Mark's fans

Note to the teacher: Use with activity 2 on page 4.

Batting Order!

In a baseball game, players bat in a certain order. Get ready to line up the events in "The King of Swing" by following the directions below.

Directions: Cut apart the ten boxes. Read the event in each box. Place all ten boxes side by side so that the events are in the correct order according to the selection. When you're finished, tape the boxes together to form one long strip. You'll discover the name of the California city in which Mark McGwire attended college.

He hit one ball over a 320-foot fence and another into the next county.

Mark began playing for the St. Louis Cardinals in 1998.

While in Alaska, Mark spent hours practicing in the batting cage.

Mark enjoyed playing lots of different sports as a boy.

After his summer in Alaska, Mark switched to playing first base.

Mark finished the season with 70 home runs.

On his first time at bat in Little League Baseball, he hit a home run.

Mark was recruited to play baseball for the University of Southern California.

Mark smashed the record when he hit his 62nd home run.

Mark pitched for his high school baseball team.

Note to the teacher: Use with activity 3 on page 4.

Name_____ *Imagery*

Imagine That!

When you read "The King of Swing," could you hear the crack of the bat and see the ball soar as Mark McGwire hit it over a fence? A good author describes a story so that you see an image in your mind. Imagery is created by using strong words—nouns, verbs, adjectives, adverbs, and phrases. Look at the example of imagery below.

The first time he was up to bat, he blasted the ball, sending it sailing over the fence for a home run.

Directions: Read each sentence below. On the blanks, make a change or changes to the sentence based on the number shown in the ball. Remember, you want to create vivid images, so use strong words! (See the examples shown.) Use a thesaurus or dictionary for help if needed.

A. He could hit the ball.

1. *He could smash the ball.*
2. *He could smash the ball out of the park.*
3. _____
4. _____

B. He started to cry.

1. _____
2. _____
3. _____
4. _____

C. The fans screamed.

1. _____
2. _____
3. _____
4. _____

Cool Connection: Pretend you are a great major-league baseball player. On the back of this sheet, write a sentence about yourself using strong imagery.

©The Education Center, Inc. • *Cornerstones of Comprehension* • TEC4104 • Key p. 79

Note to the teacher: Use with activity 5 on page 4.

7

What a Kick!

She has dark hair and **striking** good looks. Her face has been on major magazine covers. She was named one of *People* magazine's "50 Most Beautiful People in the World." She's been in many commercials. Is she a tall, graceful supermodel? Is she a pretty, famous actress? This woman isn't a model or an actress. She is soccer star Mia Hamm, a woman with a kick!

At one time, women's soccer teams played for only a few **spectators.** Many of those who watched were family members. Players trained hard to turn their teams into winners. No one paid much attention. The 1996 Olympic Games began to change that. Women's soccer became an Olympic sport for the first time. Eighty thousand fans yelled their lungs out. The U.S. women's soccer team won a gold medal. The **press** crowded around Mia after the game. The reporters wanted to hear from the team hero. As always, Mia spoke only of her team's effort.

Mia had something to **overcome** before she became an Olympic hero. She had to get over her fear of losing. Young Mia often quit playing before she would lose a game with her brothers and sisters. They got tired of her quitting. They wouldn't let Mia play unless she promised to stick out the game. She has kept that promise ever since.

Mia's **siblings** became her first soccer team. Later, the young athlete stood out on her high school team. A college coach heard about Mia. He came to watch her play. He told her coach not to tell him which player was Mia. When the game started, he spotted a player running like she had been "shot out of a cannon." He knew that must be Mia. He told her that she was good enough to become the best soccer player in the world.

Mia was asked to join the U.S. **National** Team when she was only 15 years old. She was the youngest player ever asked to join the country's soccer team. Since then, she has become the all-time leading scorer in women's soccer history. She was named the U.S. Soccer Female Athlete of the Year from 1994 to 1996. She is so good that folks call her "America's secret weapon."

Hundreds of young fans wear number nine **jerseys** at Mia's games. They scream her name when she plays. Mia gets more fan mail than any of her team members. Still, she hasn't let her **fame** go to her head. Even though she is famous, Mia is still pretty shy. She also has a sense of humor. In 1999, a Nike building was named after Mia Hamm. Her teammates teased her about it by posting signs around their hotel. The signs read "Mia Hamm Drinking Fountain" and "Mia Hamm Supply Closet." Mia teased back. She promised to have a bathroom stall named after her team's cocaptain.

Mia helped turn women's soccer into a sport with millions of fans. Now she works to help other girls on the road to soccer success. She encourages girls to **pursue,** or go after, their goals in sports. Mia wants girls to know that it's okay to be tough and **competitive.** It's okay to have the desire to win.

This tough competitor may be one of the most beautiful people in the world, but watch out for her kick! Like Mia, it's a winner.

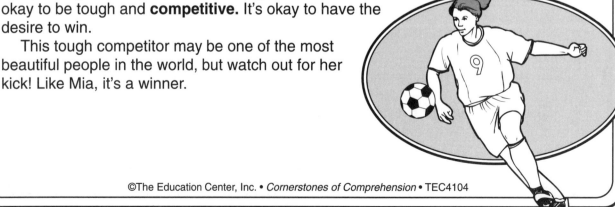

What a Kick!
Activities

1   Context Clues

Help students score points using context clues! Ahead of time, create soccer balls and goals by cutting out ten white construction paper circles (balls) and gathering ten small tissue boxes, cutting them as shown (goals). Before reading, divide students into ten groups. Assign each group a boldfaced word and give it a soccer ball, a goal, and a felt-tipped marker. Direct each group to program its ball with its assigned word and surrounding selection sentences from which it is found, and then program the top of its goal with context clues from the sentences that help define the word. Collect the balls and goals. Line up the goals on a large table or workspace. Invite a student to choose a ball and then toss it into a goal that provides clues to help define it. Finally, have the student read the word and clues and then state a definition. Continue in the same manner until all the words have been defined.

get over, fear losing

overcome

Mia had something to <u>overcome</u> before she became an Olympic hero.

She had to get over her fear of losing.

2   Fact and Opinion

Remind students that while a *fact* is a statement that can be proven, an *opinion* is based on someone's beliefs or feelings. Read the first paragraph as a class. Point out the following fact: "She was named one of *People* magazine's '50 Most Beautiful People in the World.'" Then invite students to give a related opinion, such as "Mia Hamm is beautiful." Next, provide each student with an orange construction paper cone cutout. Direct him to write a fact from the selection on one side of the cone and a related opinion on the other side. Have students share their examples. Follow up by having each student complete the activity on page 10 as directed.

Fact: Thousands of fans cheered for the U.S. team.

Opinion: Soccer is an exciting sport.

3   Idioms

Kick off a study of idioms by explaining to students that they are phrases in which the meaning of the individual words is different from the meaning of the entire phrase. Have students scan the selection for examples of idioms (*stick out the game, go to her head, on the road*). Next, list the words *run, jump,* and *kick* on the board. As a class, brainstorm idioms for each word, such as "get a running start" or "jump for joy." List the idioms and their meanings on the board. Have each student write a sentence (related to the selection) using one of the listed idioms and then illustrate it with a comical drawing. If desired, display the idiom illustrations on a bulletin board titled "We Get a Kick out of Idioms."

The players on the U.S. team <u>kicked up their heels</u> when they won the gold.

4   Summarizing

Give students a sporting chance with writing summaries! Provide each student with two 4½-inch circles cut from white and black construction paper. Direct her to cut four circles from loose-leaf paper by tracing one of the provided circles. Have her decorate the white circle (front cover) to resemble a soccer ball. Instruct the student to place the front cover atop the loose-leaf pages and black circle and then staple the resulting booklet. Next, have her summarize each paragraph in one or two sentences, writing the summary on the front and back of each page. Provide time for students to share their summaries with the class.

Jenna R.

Mia Hamm is a famous soccer player. Many people think that she is beautiful.

5   Character

Students will get a kick out of these character trait awards! Provide each student with a copy of page 11. Discuss the directions as a class. Provide time for students to complete the page. Next, divide students into six groups. Assign each group a different trait from page 11. Direct group members to use their recorded details to write a short speech about why Mia Hamm deserves the Most [character trait] Player of the Year award. Provide time for groups to present their speeches in honor of Mia.

"Fan-tastic" Facts and Opinions

Francine is fanatic about Mia! She has many opinions and wants all her friends to know them. But her friends would rather learn facts about Mia. Help Francine get her facts and opinions straight with the activity below.

Directions: Read each opinion on the left. Find the related fact on the right. Write the letter in the cone. Refer to the selection for help.

A. Women's soccer teams had only a few spectators.

B. Hundreds of young fans wear number nine jerseys and scream her name.

C. She gets more fan mail than anyone on her team.

D. She encourages girls to pursue their dreams.

E. Mia was the youngest player invited to join the U.S. National Team.

F. She became the all-time leading scorer in women's soccer history.

G. The press crowded around Mia after the game.

H. She was named one of *People* magazine's "50 Most Beautiful People in the World."

I. She spoke only of her team's efforts.

J. Mia and her teammates tease each other.

1. I think that Mia Hamm is beautiful.

2. Mia was the hero of the Olympic Games.

3. Mia is a team player.

4. Mia Hamm is the most famous player on her team.

5. When she was a teenager, Mia was much more talented than older players.

6. I think that Mia is the most talented soccer player ever.

7. Young soccer players love Mia Hamm.

8. Mia has a great sense of humor.

9. At one time, most people felt women's soccer wasn't a very popular sport.

10. Mia Hamm is a good role model.

Note to the teacher: Use with activity 2 on page 9.

On the Ball With Character Traits!

Mia Hamm certainly has talent, but her character is what makes her a star athlete. Read the traits shown on the ball below. Write a detail from the selection that proves Mia has that trait.

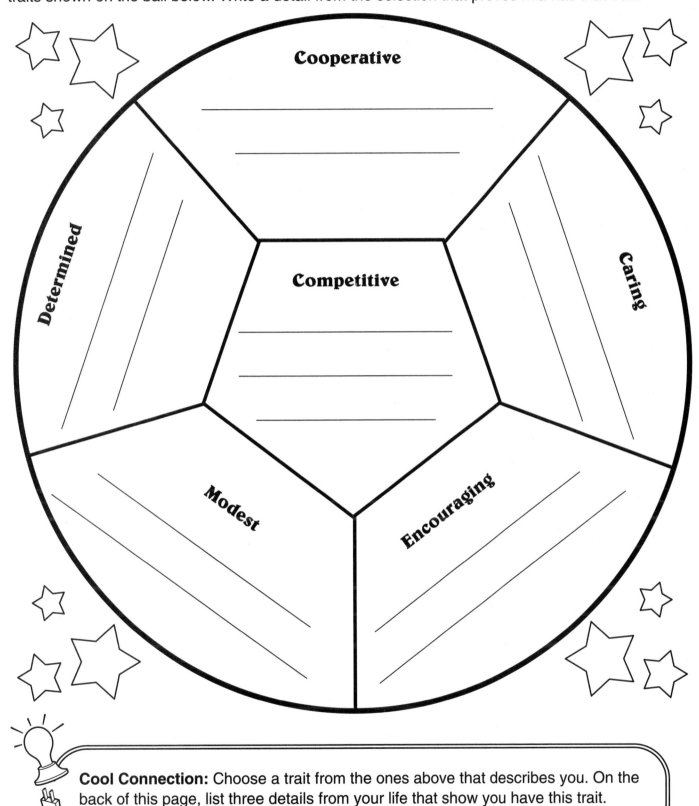

Cool Connection: Choose a trait from the ones above that describes you. On the back of this page, list three details from your life that show you have this trait.

Hang Ten!

Skateboards can be a great way to get from place to place. Riding a skateboard isn't just a way to get where you're going. It's a sport! If you're into skateboarding, you may know how it feels to trick **gravity.** Perhaps you speak **jargon** that your friends don't understand. When it comes to skateboarding, there's a lot to learn.

Skateboards have been around since the 1950s. The idea came from California surfers. They put **axles** and wheels on wooden boards so they could "surf" the streets like they surfed the waves. The idea took off. By 1964 companies had begun to produce and sell skateboards. A worldwide skateboard contest took place a year later. A new sport had been born!

Not everyone thought skating was cool. Many cities and towns passed laws against the sport. "No Skateboarding" signs popped up like weeds in a garden. The sport wasn't allowed in public streets, shopping malls, or parking garages. Skateboarders might damage **property** or hurt people. They might get hurt on someone else's property and blame the owner. New laws didn't stop skateboarding, though. Skaters found new places, like empty swimming pools, and kept on rolling.

In 1973, a wheel made of a hard, flexible plastic called **urethane** was invented. With urethane wheels, skaters could go faster. They could do new, exciting tricks. In 1975, companies began to **sponsor** and pay skaters. Skateboarding had become a **professional** sport.

The first park planned and built for skateboarding was opened in 1977. Skateparks are great places for skaters to hang ten and do other tricks. These parks often have street areas and ramps. Some tricks are done on ramps such as the *halfpipe,* which is named for its smooth, curved shape. A skater builds speed by skating down one side, up the other, and then back again. In a flash, he leaves the ramp at its top edge. The skater seems to fly briefly before gravity yanks him back down to earth.

Like most other sports, skaters use special words to talk about their sport. Golfers hope for birdies. Basketball players dribble. Skaters use jargon like *hang ten* and *goofy foot.* They do *ollies* and *grinds.* A skater might do an *ape hanger* or a *stag handstand.* This jargon may sound strange, but skaters know exactly what the words mean.

An ollie is the basis for many other tricks. It was invented by Alan "Ollie" Gelfand in 1978. When a skater is doing an ollie, he looks like he is jumping into the air with the board glued to his feet. The skater and his board hang in midair for a few seconds. In an *ollie 180,* the skater ollies and turns a half circle in the air. What a cool trick! An *ollie nosepick* sounds disgusting but it takes plenty of skill. The skater ollies onto a curb, landing and balancing on the board's nose. Then he grabs his board, jumps, and drops back to the ground. A *grind* is a noisy trick. The skater runs the board along a curb or piece of metal pipe. This makes a loud noise. There are many different kinds of grinds, such as the backside, 50/50, and feeble.

One other cool trick skaters do is put on **protective** gear. This isn't really a trick but a way to stay safe while having fun. Skaters get cuts, scrapes, and broken bones. Smart skaters wear knee and elbow pads to keep from getting badly hurt. They also wear helmets, wrist guards, and gloves.

With safety gear and practice, skaters can keep inventing fancy new tricks with weird names. The future of skateboarding will be exciting. Skaters will pop up everywhere to ride the wave of new tricks and jargon.

Hang Ten!
Activities

1 Vocabulary

Skateboarding has a vocabulary all its own. Explain that *jargon* is an informal language used mostly by a particular group. For example, skateboarders use the words *wheelie* and *kickflip* as names for tricks. Have students scan the selection for examples of skateboard jargon. List the words on the board and invite students to share their knowledge of each term. Then, after reading the selection, direct students to write a poem using skateboard jargon. Provide time for students to enhance their poems using colorful markers. Display their creations against the background of a large brown paper halfpipe.

2 Fact and Opinion

Students will be on a roll with this fun-filled fact and opinion activity. Remind students that a fact is information that can be proven (for example, "Many skateboard wheels are made of urethane"). An opinion is information or a belief that cannot be observed or proven (for example, "Skateboarding is the best sport in the world"). Provide each student with a 9" x 12" sheet of construction paper, green and yellow crayons, scissors, and glue. Then have each student complete the activity on page 14 as directed.

3 Sequence of Events

"Hang Ten!" contains several references to the development of skateboarding as a sport. After reading the selection, discuss the important changes and events that took place in the history of skateboarding. Point out that sequencing helps the reader see how events are related to each other. Then have each student complete the activity on page 15 as directed.

4 Drawing Conclusions

Have students draw conclusions about skateboard laws based on information in the selection. Invite a student to read the third paragraph aloud. Have students brainstorm a list of four or five possible laws that cities might pass against skateboarding *(no skateboarding on sidewalks, no skateboarding in school parking lots)*. Divide students into small groups. Assign each group one law from the list. Have group members brainstorm and record arguments for and against the law until there is one statement for each group member. *(For: Pedestrians might be hurt. Against: Skaters only skate after school.)* Hold a mock town meeting, providing time for each student to present his argument. Finally, hold a class vote to discover how the majority of students feel about allowing skateboarding in public areas.

5 Supporting Details

Use this art activity to get students to focus on specific details in the selection as well as the importance of skateboarding safety equipment. After reading the selection, provide each student with a large sheet of paper and crayons or markers. Have each student design a poster promoting skateboarding safety titled "No Fear! Wear Safety Gear!" Instruct students to use specific details from the selection to show safety-conscious skateboarders having fun.

No Fear! Wear Safety Gear!

...ar Safety Gear!

helmet

elbow pad

wrist brace

knee pad

14

Fact and Opinion on the Halfpipe

Directions: Read each statement. If the statement is a fact, color its skateboard green. If the statement is an opinion, color its skateboard yellow. When you finish, cut out the skateboards and the halfpipe. Glue the halfpipe on a sheet of construction paper. Then glue the fact skateboards on the left side of the halfpipe and the opinion skateboards on the right.

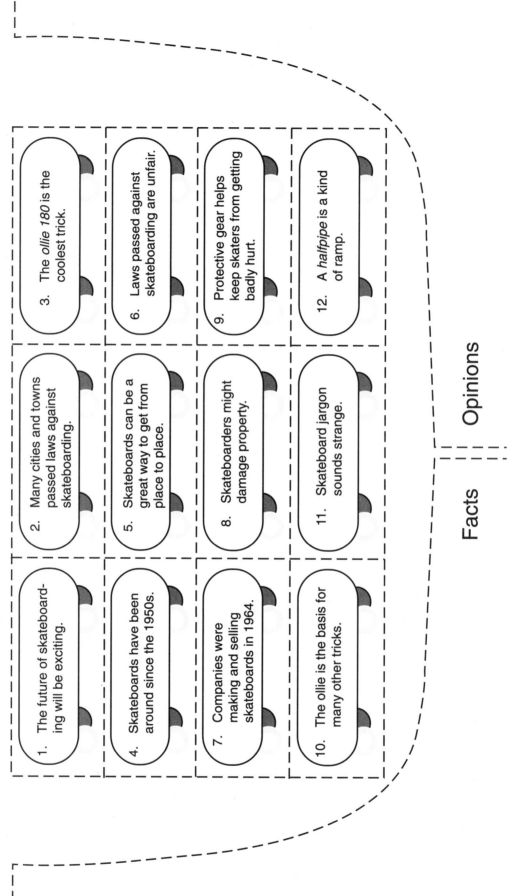

1. The future of skateboarding will be exciting.

2. Many cities and towns passed laws against skateboarding.

3. The *ollie 180* is the coolest trick.

4. Skateboards have been around since the 1950s.

5. Skateboards can be a great way to get from place to place.

6. Laws passed against skateboarding are unfair.

7. Companies were making and selling skateboards in 1964.

8. Skateboarders might damage property.

9. Protective gear helps keep skaters from getting badly hurt.

10. The ollie is the basis for many other tricks.

11. Skateboard jargon sounds strange.

12. A *halfpipe* is a kind of ramp.

Facts

Opinions

Note to the teacher: Use with activity 2 on page 13.

Name _____

Sidewalk Surfing Sequence

Directions: "Surf" the selection to find the important changes and events that took place in the development of skateboarding. In the box provided, write a full sentence to explain why each date is important. The first one has been done for you.

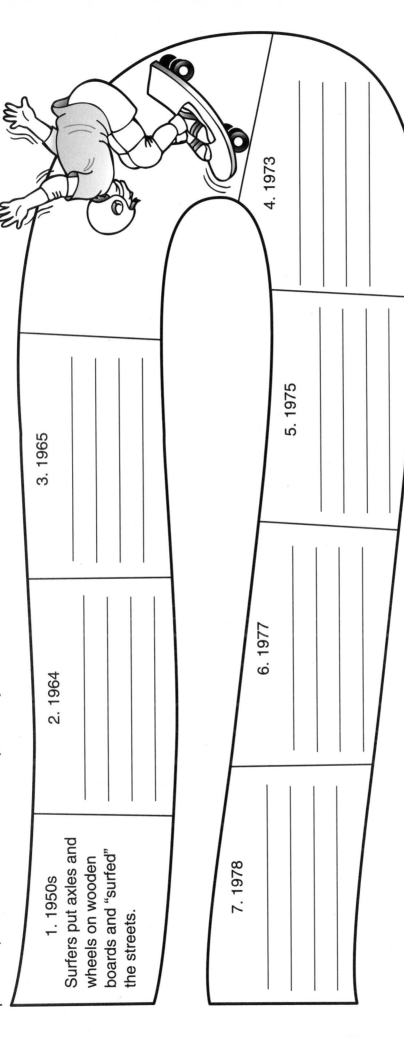

1. 1950s

Surfers put axles and wheels on wooden boards and "surfed" the streets.

2. 1964

3. 1965

4. 1973

5. 1975

6. 1977

7. 1978

Cool Connection: The first skateboarders were surfers. They probably didn't wear safety gear when they started surfing the streets. On the back of this sheet, write a paragraph telling how changes in the sport have made it important to wear protective gear. Be sure to support your ideas with facts from the selection.

©The Education Center, Inc. • *Cornerstones of Comprehension* • TEC4104 • Key p. 79

Note to the teacher: Use with activity 3 on page 13.

An Ordinary Kid

Beverly Bunn was an **ordinary** kid. She slid down stair railings and slept under the stars. She liked clowns, Ferris wheels, and movies. So what would an ordinary kid like Beverly want to be when she grew up? A ballet dancer? An actress? How about a writer? That's just what this **spunky** girl became. Beverly Bunn is none other than the famous writer, Beverly Cleary.

Beverly was born in 1916. She lived with her parents on the family farm in Oregon. She was a wiggler and a **wanderer.** Her grandfather sometimes paid her a nickel just to sit still for five minutes. Once Beverly's father told her that the earth was round like an orange. That gave her the idea to walk around the world. Soon after she started, her father caught up with her and told her about the world's size. Another time, Beverly went to find the pot of gold she'd heard was at the end of a rainbow. Then her mother explained that it didn't really exist.

Farm life kept Beverly busy. She watched cows being milked and sheep being sheared. She teased the chickens and collected their eggs. She picked buttercups, foxgloves, and bachelor's buttons. Sometimes Beverly did more than just pick the flowers. Once she sewed bachelor's buttons onto her father's sweater to replace missing buttons.

Beverly's family moved to Portland when she was six. The big city was an exciting place. Elevators and escalators rose and fell in the tall buildings. There were lots of children. Beverly and her new friends roller-skated, walked on **stilts,** and skinned their knees. Portland even had a library where her mother read to her. Beverly couldn't wait to start first grade and learn to read by herself.

At first, learning to read was easy for Beverly. Then she got chicken pox and missed school. Later that year she came down with **smallpox.** She fell behind because she was absent so much. Beverly began to hate school and reading. She thought that school books were boring. They didn't have any stories about children like herself and her friends. In third grade, Beverly finally found some books that she enjoyed. She read *The Story of Dr. Dolittle* and wrote a **review** about it, which was published with her picture in the newspaper.

Her love of reading grew stronger. She **scoured** the library for funny and exciting stories about children, but they were **rare.** Beverly also enjoyed writing. Her seventh-grade teacher praised her talent. "When Beverly grows up, she should write children's books," the teacher declared.

When Beverly grew up, she became a librarian herself. She wrote her first book, *Henry Huggins,* which was published in 1950. Since then, she has written over 30 books and won many awards. Beverly's books are the kind she longed to read about—real kids doing really funny things. Some of her ideas came from funny things that happened to her own twin sons. Even Klickitat Street, where most of her characters live, is a real street in Portland.

Today, **sculptures** of Beverly's characters play in a garden four blocks from Klickitat Street. One is of Ramona Quimby, the spunky little girl with the vivid imagination. Ramona gets off to a rough start in school. She once gets lost on a **quest** to find the end of the rainbow. When you think about it, Ramona seems to have a lot in common with her creator. The sculpture shows Ramona with her head back and her arms thrown open. Perhaps she is showing her delight that there are wonderful books by Beverly Cleary for children everywhere to enjoy!

An Ordinary Kid
Activities

1 Prior Knowledge

Spark students' interest in the selection with this prereading activity. Begin by writing the title of the selection on the chalkboard. Discuss the meaning of the word *ordinary*. Then invite students to suggest traits (such as energetic) and activities (such as going to school, playing video games, etc.) of ordinary kids. List at least 15 responses on the chalkboard. Point out that the ordinary kid who is the subject of the selection was born in 1916. Then have students reread the listed traits and activities and decide which would not apply to a child growing up in that time period (such as playing video games). Erase these from the list. Discuss other traits and activities that might be representative of the early 1900s and add them to the list. After reading, review the list and discuss ways the information helped students understand the selection.

2 Vocabulary

Familiarize students with vocabulary words in the selection with this activity. Begin by reading aloud the boldfaced words in the selection. Invite volunteers to share what they know about each word's meaning and to use it in an original sentence. For unknown words, appoint a student to act as a definition consultant to identify the meanings using a dictionary. Follow up by having each student complete the activity on page 18 as directed. (Each student will need scissors, glue, a yellow crayon, and access to a dictionary.)

3 Comparing and Contrasting

Use this activity to help students compare and contrast information about Beverly Cleary's experiences. Begin by reminding students that comparisons show how things are similar, while contrasts show how things are different. Write the clue words shown below on the chalkboard. Tell students that clue words can be used to emphasize comparisons and contrasts. Share the example sentences and have a volunteer reword each one using a clue word for emphasis. Divide the class into small groups and provide each group with a sheet of chart paper. Direct the groups to work together to scan the selection for details that can be compared or contrasted. Have them rewrite the details using clue words, recording their responses on the chart paper. Provide time for groups to share their work.

Comparison Clue Words
also   both   similarly   too
Beverly and Ramona were spunky. *Both Beverly and Ramona were spunky.*

Contrast Clue Words
but   however   rather   unlike
Beverly was an only child. Ramona had an older sister. *Beverly was an only child, but Ramona had an older sister.*

4 Main Idea and Supporting Details

Have students focus their attention on main idea and supporting details with this activity. Remind students that the main idea of a selection is its central theme or main message. Invite a student to identify the main idea of the selection. *(Beverly Cleary's childhood experiences and feelings led her to write books that appeal to children everywhere.)* Then ask students to share several details that support the statement. Next, point out that in longer reading selections, paragraph topics often serve to support the overall main idea and have supporting details of their own. Discuss examples of main ideas and supporting details from several paragraphs. Follow up by having each student complete the activity on page 19 as directed.

5 Author's Purpose

The author's purpose in writing the selection is to inform the reader about Beverly Cleary's life. Use this activity to discuss the author's purpose in writing the selection and to motivate students to do some creative writing of their own. Begin by telling students that Beverly won an essay contest as a child. She was the only child who entered. This experience taught her a valuable lesson: the way to become a writer is to try writing. Remind students that many of Beverly's stories are based on her childhood memories. Have each student complete the graphic organizer on page 20 as directed. Then have her use the completed organizer to write a short fictional story of her own.

Name_____   *Vocabulary*

Words Worth Their Weight in Gold

Directions: Read the definitions shown below. Use a yellow crayon to color the pots at the bottom of the page. Cut them out and match them with their definitions. Then glue them in place.

1. poles with foot supports that lift a person above the ground when he or she is walking

2. report about the content and/or quality of a book, movie, or play

3. figures or statues made of chiseled stone, carved wood, metal, or other materials

4. scarce, not often found

5. typical or normal

6. having a brave or courageous spirit

7. an exciting journey taken to hunt or search for something

8. searched quickly but completely

9. a serious disease that causes skin sores, a high fever, and chills

10. a person who moves or roams from place to place

©The Education Center, Inc. • *Cornerstones of Comprehension* • TEC4104 • Key p. 79

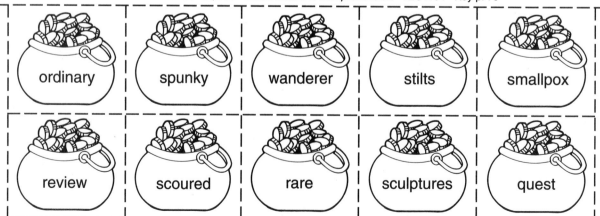

18   **Note to the teacher:** Use with activity 2 on page 17.

Neighborhood Details

Part 1: Read the main idea shown on each house below. Then find two details in the selection that support each main idea and write them on the lines provided.

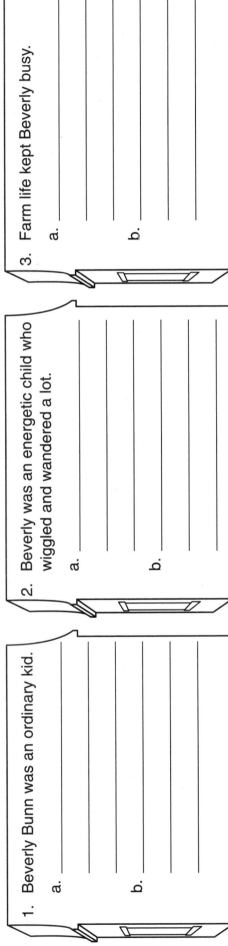

1. Beverly Bunn was an ordinary kid.

   a. _____

   b. _____

2. Beverly was an energetic child who wiggled and wandered a lot.

   a. _____

   b. _____

3. Farm life kept Beverly busy.

   a. _____

   b. _____

Part 2: Read each pair of details shown below. Then write a main-idea sentence for each pair.

1. Main idea: _____

   a. Elevators and escalators rose and fell in the tall buildings.

   b. Portland even had a library.

2. Main idea: _____

   a. Then she got chicken pox and missed school.

   b. Later that year she came down with smallpox.

3. Main idea: _____

   a. Ramona gets off to a rough start in school.

   b. She once gets lost on a quest to find the end of the rainbow.

Note to the teacher: Use with activity 4 on page 17.

Name _____

20

A Funny Thing Happened

Beverly Cleary writes about children and the funny things that happen to them. Think about something funny that has happened to you or someone you know. Then use this sheet to capture the details of the event and write a funny story like Beverly Cleary might write!

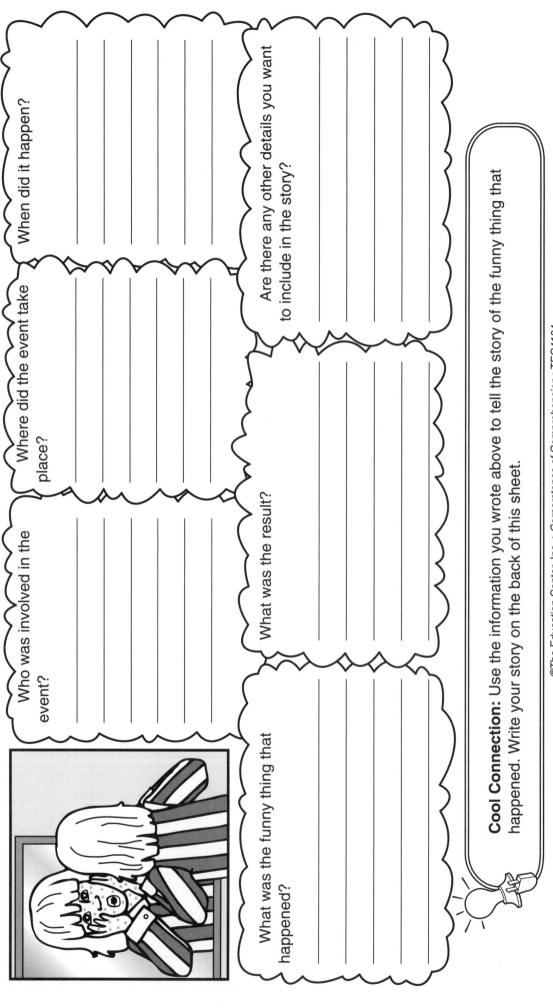

Who was involved in the event?

Where did the event take place?

When did it happen?

What was the funny thing that happened?

What was the result?

Are there any other details you want to include in the story?

Cool Connection: Use the information you wrote above to tell the story of the funny thing that happened. Write your story on the back of this sheet.

Note to the teacher: Use with activity 5 on page 17.

A Special Spark

Women from the town waited for hours in front of the church. Some were curious. Others were angry. They were rudely silent when they caught sight of the young woman in the black silk dress. The woman was about to make history. That day, Elizabeth Blackwell received her **diploma** from the president of Geneva Medical College. She became the first woman doctor in modern times.

Elizabeth was born into a wealthy English family on February 3, 1821. Back then most children of wealthy families were taught at home. Boys and girls learned different things. Young ladies learned about art, sewing, and music. Young men were taught Latin, math, and astronomy. Elizabeth's father felt that his girls should be taught just like the boys. So Elizabeth studied the same subjects as her brothers. She read books from her father's library. She worked hard, often late into the night.

When Elizabeth was 11 years old, her family moved to America. It took the sailing ship almost two months to cross the ocean. Elizabeth and most of the other passengers were seasick much of the time. They arrived in New York at the time a deadly cholera **epidemic** was sweeping through the city. Many people left out of fear of the often deadly disease. The family moved several times before finally settling in Ohio. When Elizabeth was 17, her father became ill and died. Soon after, her aunt died of the same disease that had taken Mr. Blackwell's life. For the next few years, Elizabeth helped to support her family by teaching.

Then a visit to a dying friend changed Elizabeth's life. The woman felt that **suffering** would have been easier to bear if she had a woman for a doctor. But there were no woman doctors. As they talked, the woman suggested that Elizabeth study **medicine.** At first, Elizabeth was shocked by the idea. Then she began to think about how much female doctors were needed. Could she really become a doctor?

Elizabeth made up her mind. She knew becoming a doctor would not be easy. Medical school was **expensive.** Again, Elizabeth took a job teaching. She lived in the home of a former doctor, John Dickson, and studied his medical books. Elizabeth taught during the day and studied medicine at night. People warned her that a woman would not be **accepted** into medical school. She began to apply anyway.

Elizabeth wrote to school after school. Twenty-eight schools turned her down. Then, in October 1847, she was thrilled to get a letter from Geneva Medical College. She had been accepted! The other students had been told about Elizabeth. It was left to them to vote for or against her. The students may have thought their teachers were joking. They all voted for her. To their great surprise, a "lady student" soon appeared at the school.

During the summer after her first term, Elizabeth worked hard. She was a **volunteer** in a hospital for the poor. It was there that a special spark began to burn inside her. Her heart went out to the sick women she treated. When she went to see the **patients,** the young male doctors would leave. This made Elizabeth just work harder. She finished first in her class.

Elizabeth's spark burned brightly for many years. She opened a clinic for poor women and children. She started a women's medical college. She was friends with Florence Nightingale, a famous nurse. Elizabeth and Florence taught people that they could help prevent sickness by eating well and staying clean. Elizabeth Blackwell sparked changes in health care. She led the way for women to enter new fields of work. She was a **pioneer** in medicine and women's rights and is still a role model for women today.

A Special Spark
Activities

1 Vocabulary

Students will get the message about vocabulary meanings with this group activity! In advance, program one index card for each boldfaced selection word. Then divide students into three groups. Give each group three word cards. Follow the steps below to complete the activity.

1. Each group defines its words (as used in the selection) and records the definitions on the cards.
2. Members of each group sit in a row.
3. The first student reads one word and its definition to the student behind him.
4. Each student, in turn, relays the "message" to the person behind him.
5. The last student relays the message to the first student, who checks the meaning and then moves to the front for the next round of play.
6. Rotate words among groups and continue play until each group has relayed the meanings of all nine words.

2 Predictions

Before reading the selection, prepare an unprogrammed diagram (similar to the one shown) on a sheet of chart paper. Label the inner circle "1800s." Label the outer circle "[current year]." Next, explain to students that many years ago women didn't enter certain professions. Have students brainstorm a list of jobs held by women today. Record responses in the outer circle. Then guide the class to decide what jobs they think would have been held by women in the 1800s. List these jobs in the inner circle. Tell students that the selection is about a woman who helped open the field of medicine to women. If desired, continue the discussion by having students predict problems this woman might have faced as she entered this male-dominated field; then have students read the selection to determine if their predictions were correct.

2003
1800s
nurse
seamstress
teacher
doctor
politician
police officer

3 Judgments

Elizabeth Blackwell was turned down by 28 medical schools. The school administrators had made the judgment that a woman should not be admitted. Remind students that a *judgment* is a decision about whether an action is right or wrong. Explain that a judgment is considered *valid* if evidence supports the statement and *invalid* if it does not. Then have each student complete the activity on page 23 as directed. After students have completed the page, invite them to share their responses with the class.

4 Drawing Conclusions

Give your students practice drawing conclusions with this after-reading activity. First, explain to students that an author sometimes conveys a message to a reader without saying it directly. Readers must use details and personal experiences to determine what is not actually stated. Share the following example from the selection: "When she went to see the patients, the young male doctors would leave." Guide students to conclude that the male doctors in the hospital who left when Elizabeth entered a room probably didn't respect her or feel that a woman should be allowed to practice medicine. Follow up by having each student complete the activity on page 24 as directed.

5 Sequence of Events

Students will have sequencing events bagged with this activity! To prepare, gather three paper lunch bags and a class supply of jumbo craft sticks. Program each bag with one of the following headings: "Before Elizabeth's medical training," "During Elizabeth's medical training," or "After Elizabeth's medical training." Draw female facial features beneath the programming on each bag. Cut a slit for the mouth. Give each student one craft stick. Have him write one event from Elizabeth's life on the stick. Collect the sticks. Then have each student, in turn, take a stick (not his own), read the event, and place it in the appropriate bag. If desired, place the bags and craft sticks at a center for future use.

Before Elizabeth's medical training

• Elizabeth opened a women's college.

Think Before You Judge!

Years ago, many people believed that women shouldn't study medicine. Elizabeth Blackwell had her heart set on becoming a doctor. But 28 medical schools turned her away. The administrators who didn't admit Elizabeth may have made *judgments* about her like those shown below. What could she have said to help them understand that their judgments were invalid?

Directions: Read each judgment listed below. Find details in the selection that make the judgments *invalid,* or incorrect. Then write what Elizabeth would have said on the lines provided.

Judgment 1: A woman isn't educated enough to go to medical school.

1. _____
_____
_____

Judgment 2: A woman isn't familiar with sickness and disease.

2. _____
_____
_____

Judgment 3: A woman is weak and can't work as hard as a man.

3. _____
_____
_____

Judgment 4: A woman can't earn enough money to go to medical school.

4. _____
_____
_____

Judgment 5: People don't want to be treated by female doctors.

5. _____
_____
_____

Cool Connection: Pretend you are Elizabeth Blackwell. On the back of this sheet, write a business letter to an imaginary medical school. Use information from this page to persuade the school administrator to admit you as a medical student.

And I Quote...

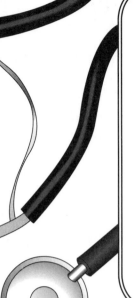

a. dying friend
b. college president
c. male doctor
d. Elizabeth's father
e. woman from town
f. Florence Nightingale
g. male medical students
h. John Dickson

Cool Connection: Pretend you are Elizabeth Blackwell. On the back of this sheet, finish each imaginary quote with something Elizabeth might have said.
1. "When my family arrived in New York City…"
2. "When I got the letter of acceptance to Geneva Medical College…"
3. "When the college president gave me my diploma…"

Directions: Read each of the imaginary quotes below. Choose from the list on the right the person who might have made each statement. Write the matching letter from the list in the box. Explain your answer on the blank provided.

☐ 1. "I would never dream of becoming a doctor! What kind of woman is she?"

_____

☐ 2. "We didn't think you would really come here to study."

_____

☐ 3. "Elizabeth Blackwell, please come forward to receive your diploma."

_____

☐ 4. "I have many medical books for you to study."

_____

☐ 5. "We must keep the hospitals clean to stop the spread of disease."

_____

☐ 6. "That woman doctor just got here. I'm leaving. I'll see my patients later."

_____

☐ 7. "My illness would have been easier on me if I'd had a woman for a doctor."

_____

☐ 8. "You will study Latin, math, and astronomy like your brothers."

_____

©The Education Center, Inc. • *Cornerstones of Comprehension* • TEC4104 • Key p. 79

Note to the teacher: Use with activity 4 on page 22.

A Scarecrow of a Man

Abraham Lincoln was a long-legged, gangly man. He had big ears and a scrawny neck. His head seemed too small for his six-foot four-inch frame. His black stovepipe hat, which he kept stuffed with papers, made him seem even taller. His sleeves were too long. His pants were too short. He looked like a scarecrow of a man.

Abe didn't worry about people laughing at him. He had plenty of **confidence.** He laughed at himself. Once, another **politician** called Abe two-faced. "If I had another face, would I wear this one?" he joked.

Abe looked very serious, but he liked to laugh. When he met with the men in his **cabinet,** he often read to them from funny books. Some of the men got mad at him for wasting their time. Abe knew that humor wasn't a waste of time. It helped him to "whistle down sadness."

The 1860s were sad times indeed for the United States. The country was divided. The Southern states allowed slavery. The Northern states did not. Lincoln said that "a house divided against itself" could not stand. He was right. Shortly after he was elected president, the country split apart.

The Southern states did not think Lincoln represented them. After all, he had tried to stop the spread of slavery. Eleven Southern states **seceded** from the **Union.** They formed their own government called the Confederate States of America.

War broke out when the **Southern** states fired on a U.S. fort in South Carolina. As **commander in chief,** Lincoln took charge of the armed forces. He ran the Civil War from his office on the second floor of the White House. He met with generals to direct the army. He visited soldiers. He hoped that the war would be over soon.

Lincoln's main goal for fighting the Civil War was to save the union of states. He thought that the United States was the "last, best hope" for liberty, or freedom, in the world. He wanted to show that a nation in which all men were equal could **endure.** As the Civil War raged, Lincoln began to realize that slaves had to be freed. If not, the war would settle nothing.

Back then, the **Constitution** protected slavery. Each state could decide to allow or **abolish** slavery. Lincoln hated slavery, but his deepest hope was to bring the states back together. In September of 1862, Lincoln gave the Southern states one last chance to keep their slaves. He told them that they must **rejoin** the union of states by January 1, 1863. When they refused, Lincoln signed a **proclamation.** It said that all Southern slaves were free. "I never in my life felt more certain that I was doing right, than I do in signing this paper," Lincoln said.

Since there was no way to enforce the order, it didn't really free any slaves. It did give them hope. More and more were able to escape. During the next year, nearly 200,000 former slaves joined the Northern army. With their help, the North won the war in 1865.

Lincoln felt that his most important act as president was freeing the slaves. When the war was over, it was time to rebuild the nation. Lincoln never got a chance to help "bind up the nation's wounds." Just five days after the war ended, John Wilkes Booth shot and killed President Lincoln.

Lincoln was a scarecrow of a man who did great things. He struggled to keep the American states united. He fought for freedom and equality. He helped end slavery. He gave his life for his country.

A Scarecrow of a Man

Activities

1 Vocabulary

Introduce students to the vocabulary in the selection with a fun prereading activity. Pair students and assign each twosome one of the words listed below.

Secede	Secede
to stop suddenly	to leave an organization

Then give each pair a sheet of chart paper that has been labeled with its word as shown. Have the twosome look up the word's meaning and secretly write it on either half of the paper. On the other half, have the pair write a false meaning. When groups are finished, have each pair share its chart and challenge the class to guess the correct definition. At the end of the activity, have each pair cut apart its two definitions and post the correct one in the room to use as a reference during reading.

politician	commander in chief	abolish
cabinet	armed forces	confidence
represent	Union	proclamation
rejoin	endure	enforce
secede	Constitution	equality

2 Connotation and Denotation

Use this activity to help students more fully understand the selection by examining the differences between the *denotations* and *connotations* of words. Begin by explaining that words may have two kinds of meanings. The denotation is the dictionary meaning and the connotation is a suggested meaning. Discuss the positive and negative connotations of the word *slave* using the following sentences: "Harriet Tubman was a former slave." "Ryan was a slave to his garden." Guide students to understand that Harriet Tubman had no choice about living as a slave. Ryan appeared to love working in his garden although it took up much of his time. Follow up by having each student complete the activity on page 27 as directed.

3 Classifying and Categorizing

Help students locate and categorize the selection's details about Honest Abe with this group activity. After each student reads the selection, divide the class into groups. Have each group cut three sheets of notebook paper in the shape of a stovepipe hat. Instruct students to label one cutout "Physical Traits," one "Character Traits," and one "Actions" as shown. Next, direct each group to skim the selection and list appropriate details about Lincoln on each cutout. After sharing students' findings, have each group trace one of the hat cutouts onto black paper and cut out the tracing. Then have the students staple the black cutout on top of the other three to make a booklet.

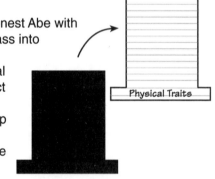

Physical Traits

4 Main Idea

Abraham Lincoln made headlines in his time, and so can your students with the help of this main idea activity! First, review that the main idea of a paragraph can be found in the topic sentence. Remind students that the topic sentence can occur anywhere in the paragraph. Next, have each student number the paragraphs on his copy of the selection from 1 to 11. Then have each student complete the activity on page 28 as directed.

5 Drawing Conclusions

Explain that authors sometimes use clues to convey messages to readers indirectly. The reader combines the clues with experience and common sense to draw a conclusion. Invite a student to read the first paragraph aloud. Point out that a reader might conclude that Lincoln had trouble finding clothes that fit. Next, divide the class into small groups. Give each group a sheet of chart paper and a pad of self-sticking notes. Instruct students to label their posters as shown and to search the selection for evidence that Lincoln possessed each trait. Have students write each detail on a separate note and stick it under the appropriate trait. Provide time for groups to share their work.

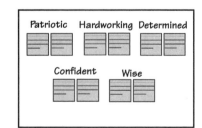

Plus or Minus

Every word has a dictionary meaning, or *denotation*. Many words have a second kind of meaning, called a *connotation*. A connotation is related to the feeling or picture you might get from the word. It can be a positive or negative feeling.

Part 1: Read each word below from the selection. Brainstorm the feelings or images you think of when you hear this word. Write your ideas in the blanks.

1. ☆ confidence _____

2. ☆ equality _____

3. ☆ slave _____

4. ☆ war _____

5. ☆ freedom _____

6. ☆ hate _____

Part 2: In the star beside each word above, draw a plus sign if you think the connotation is positive. Draw a minus sign if you think the connotation is negative.

Part 3: Choose six other words from the selection that you feel have a positive connotation. Write one word in each blank.

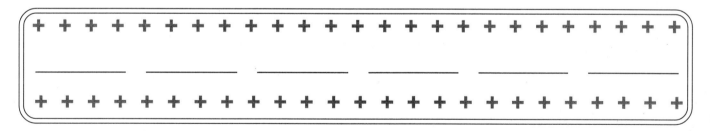

Cool Connection: Choose one of the words from Part 3. Draw a picture that illustrates the denotation of the word.

Headline News

Abraham Lincoln certainly made headlines in his time. You can too by following the directions below!

Directions: Select five paragraphs (other than the last paragraph) from the reading selection. Write the number of each paragraph in a small box below. Then identify the main idea of each paragraph and write it as a newspaper headline in one of the papers. For example, the headline for the first paragraph might read "Man Mistaken for Scarecrow!" In each big box, draw a picture that illustrates the headline.

Lincoln's Memory Lives

☐ ## Greenville Gazette

_____
_____
_____

☐ ## Potterton Press

_____
_____
_____

☐ ## Jarvisville Journal

_____
_____
_____
_____

☐ ## The Tipton Times

_____
_____
_____
_____

☐ ## Denton Daily Star

_____
_____
_____
_____

Cool Connection: Pretend you've been hired to write a movie based on the selection. You cannot include Abraham Lincoln's name in the title. What would you title the movie and why? On the back of this sheet, draw a poster to advertise the film using details from the selection.

Bloodthirsty Bats

Night blankets a field. Cattle graze on the land that was once part of a dense rain forest. The air is hot, heavy. The bright, round moon casts long, fat shadows of the cows snoozing in the grass. A hunter drops out of the sky. Its wings of thin, stretchy skin are open like an umbrella. It lands nearby, but the cows don't stir.

The tiny hunter silently **stalks** its sleeping victim. It is grayish brown, furry, and as small as a mouse. Its teeth are as sharp as razors. The hunter moves closer to the cow, walking on tiptoes like a strange ballet dancer. Then it uses its strong muscles to leap onto its victim. Heat **sensors** in its nose help it find a blood vessel close to the cow's skin. It bites, but the cow doesn't wake up. The tiny hunter laps up the blood flowing from the cut.

What kind of creature wings through the night to dine on cow's blood? *Desmodus rotundus,* the **vampire bat.** Vampire bats have been around for six to eight million years. We know from **fossil** records that there used to be more than the three kinds of vampire bats that exist today. The white-winged and the hairy-legged vampire bats feed on bird blood. The common vampire bat prefers the blood of large **mammals.** It does not drink enough blood to really harm the animals. A vampire bat only needs about two tablespoons of blood a day.

You might be wondering whether vampire bats bite humans. Myths, legends, and movies tell of vampire bats that bite the necks of humans and drink their blood. There have been some reports of common vampire bats biting people. The truth is that bats are more likely to get their midnight snacks from cows, pigs, and horses.

Vampire bats are found only in Mexico, Central America, and South America. Europe may be the home of vampire myths and legends, but it has no real vampire bats. In fact, when vampire bats were first found, they were named after the creature in the legends. Vampire bats are not evil monsters. They are just **parasites** that need the blood of other animals in order to survive.

While their feeding habits may not seem friendly to the cows and pigs they snack on, vampire bats are friendly with their own kind. About 100 bats live together in a group called a **colony.** Groups of bats hunt together and groom each other. A vampire bat will even share its own food with a buddy who is hungry!

Vampire bats hang out in caves, tree hollows, houses, and empty buildings. Bats hang upside down when they **roost,** or rest. Their sharp, curved claws help them cling tightly so they don't fall. Hanging upside down is handy when they need to make a quick getaway. They just let go and fly away!

People do have a good reason to be careful around vampire bats. Like other bat species, they can spread diseases such as **rabies** to humans and animals. This makes them scary enough to cause ranchers and farmers to try to get rid of them. For this reason, **livestock** owners often try to destroy places where bats roost. On the other hand, bats may prove to be very helpful to humans. Their saliva is very special because it helps blood flow. It has been used to make a drug called Draculin, which might be used someday to treat heart patients.

Vampire bats may seem like creepy creatures of the night. They may even remind you of scary legends. But next Halloween when you see a vampire bat decoration, remember that these bloodthirsty creatures are not so bad after all.

Bloodthirsty Bats

Activities

1 Vocabulary

Build your class's bat background before reading the selection with this vocabulary matching game. Ahead of time, cut out the cards on page 31. Then give each student one card. (If desired, make and cut out 30 bat shapes and have each student glue her card to a bat shape.) Have the class listen carefully as each student, in turn, reads aloud what is written on her card. Direct the students holding matching words, definitions, and context sentences to locate each other and stand together as a group. When each group has formed, direct each student to read her card to the class. Then congratulate the groups for doing a "bat-iful" job!

2 Multiple-Meaning Words

Students will go batty for this multiple-meaning word activity! Remind students that some words have multiple meanings. Give the following example from the selection: "The cows don't stir." Explain that stir, in this case, means to move, but stir can also mean to mix. Have students scan the selection for multiple-meaning words. List them on the board. Then direct each

The cow is stirring a spoon while it is stirring.

student to choose one word from the list and draw a comical picture showing the two meanings of that word as shown. Finally, have each student share her drawing and explain the meanings of the word. (*Multiple-meaning words in the selection include* blankets, casts, cut, wake, laps, kind, bat, records, *and* groom.)

3 Classify and Categorize

Help your students organize the bat facts from the selection with this classifying activity. First, have each student draw two large bat shapes on a sheet of drawing paper. Then direct the student to label one bat "Bat Traits" and the other "Bat Behaviors." Instruct each student to reread the selection, paying close attention to the facts that relate to the two categories. Finally, have the student record the information about bats in the appropriate bat shape. Encourage students to list at least four facts in each category.

4 Figurative Language

Students will hang on every word they read with this fun figurative language activity! Remind students that *figurative language* is the use of words that have a hidden meaning rather than a literal one. Then have each student complete page 32 as directed. Watch as your students' understanding of figurative language devices takes off like a colony of bats from its roost!

5 Tone

Appeal to your students' scientific sides as you investigate the selection's *tone,* or mood. Ask a student to read the first two paragraphs aloud, while the rest of the class listens carefully to identify the tone. *(scary)* Discuss the words that contribute to the tone. Ask a different student to read the third paragraph. Again, challenge students to listen and identify words that set the tone. *(scientific/informative)* Then provide each student with a 9" x 12" sheet of black construction paper, a white crayon, and scissors. Instruct each student to cut out a large bat shape. Then have him read the rest of the selection, listing the words that set the scary tone on one side of the shape and the scientific tone on the other. If desired, have each student tape his bat to a classroom wall or window, displaying the side that shows which tone he prefers.

mammals	warm-blooded vertebrates	The common vampire bat feeds on **mammals** such as cows and pigs.
vampire bat	flying mammal that feeds on the blood of other animals	The **vampire bat** crept silently toward its victim.
parasite	animal or plant that lives off another and gets food from it	A vampire bat is a **parasite** that feeds on other animals.
rabies	fatal disease	The farmer was afraid the bat might be infected with **rabies.**
roost	to sleep or rest	Bats **roost** in caves during the day.
sensors	things that detect heat, sound, or pressure	The bat's **sensors** help it find the warm blood of an animal.
stalk	hunt or track a person or animal in a quiet, secret way	A vampire bat will silently **stalk** its prey.
fossil	remains of a living thing preserved in the earth's crust	The hairy-legged vampire bat **fossil** was found in South America.
livestock	farm animals kept for use and profit	The **livestock** that sleep outside are easy prey for the vampire bats.
colony	group of living things with common characteristics	The **colony** of vampire bats hunted together.

Figuratively Speaking!

Think about a book or story in which you felt as if you could see the place, person, or thing being described. Writers often use a type of figurative language called *imagery* to express ideas in a vivid way for the reader. For example, an image of nighttime is created with the sentence "Night blankets a field."

Part 1: Draw a line to match each simple sentence on the left to its corresponding imagery-rich sentence on the right.

1. The bat flies downward.
2. There was a full moon.
3. It flies in the dark sky.
4. The bat walks up to the cow.

A. The tiny hunter stalks its sleeping victim.
B. A hunter drops out of the sky.
C. The bright, round moon casts long, fat shadows.
D. It wings through the night.

Part 2: To paint pictures for the reader, writers also use *similes.* A simile compares two things using *like* or *as.* Look back in the selection to find three similes. Write one in the top of each box below. In the last box, create a simile of your own about a vampire bat. Then illustrate each of the similes.

1.

2.

3.

4.

Living Dinosaurs

"Terrible lizards" soared and stomped across the earth between 230 and 65 million years ago. Some of them were small and weighed only four pounds. Some were huge and weighed up to 160,000 pounds. Some ate meat. Others ate plants. They had one thing in common. Dinosaurs, as these reptiles are called, suddenly died out about 65 million years ago. Or did they?

In 1938, some fishermen caught a five-foot-long fish. It was pale pink and blue with shiny silver markings. The men gave the fish to a woman who ran a **museum.** She looked in some books and found a picture that looked like the fish. It turned out to be a **coelacanth.** These fish were thought to have died out about 70 million years ago!

The **tuatara** could also be called a living dinosaur. This small reptile is found on several islands near **New Zealand.** The tuatara has a bony arch on its skull behind its eyes. It has a third eye on the top of its head. The bony arch proves that this rare reptile is a living dinosaur. It is a survivor of a family that died out 60 million years ago.

The **Komodo** dragon is an animal that looks as if it just walked out of a movie. It is not really a dragon, but it is the largest living lizard. Some say Komodo dragons can grow up to 30 feet long. The biggest one ever measured was over ten feet long. Komodo dragons are meat eaters with jagged teeth and long, sharp claws. They were found during the First World War. A plane crashed near an island in Southeast Asia. The pilot saw giant reptiles living there. Back home, no one believed his tales about the monster reptiles. Now we know they are very real!

Crocodiles are also a kind of living dinosaur. Crocodiles lived at the same time as the tyrannosaurus and brontosaurus—as much as 200 million years ago! They lived through the breakup of the **continents.** They lived through the **Ice Ages.** Today's crocodiles have not changed much. They still look as if they could have lived at the same time as the tyrannosaurus.

The coelacanth, tuatara, Komodo dragon, and crocodile prove that some kinds of dinosaurs are still alive and well. But there is little proof for another kind of living dinosaur. There have been reports of an animal that looks like a dinosaur living in the African Congo. This animal, if it exists at all, is still a mystery. No one has been able to find so much as a skeleton of it! Still, plenty of people claim to have seen the creature, which is known as the **mokele-mbembe.**

The mokele-mbembe is said to be a reddish-brown, 30-foot-long animal. It has an elephant-sized body, a long neck, and three toes on each foot. It spends most of its life in the waters of the African Congo. In the 1980s scientists went searching for it.

Are there flying dinosaurs today? Several schoolteachers said that a huge flying creature swooped down near their cars in 1976. It had a 12-foot wingspan. When they looked it up in the school library, they thought that it might have been a **pterosaur.** Pterosaurs were flying reptiles that lived long, long ago. Why was a pterosaur flying around 65 million years after it was supposed to have died?

Most of the dinosaurs died out long ago. Some dinosaur-like animals still live. Some are still a mystery. Others live only in our imaginations. One thing is for sure, though. Dinosaurs are some of the most interesting creatures that ever lived!

Living Dinosaurs

Activities

1   Vocabulary

Before reading "Living Dinosaurs," use this activity to review the vocabulary. Ahead of time, program ten index cards with the boldfaced words. Place a dinosaur cutout, a globe, and a clock at the front of the room. Explain that students will sort the ten words from the selection into three categories: creatures, places, and times. Show each card, in turn, and read the word aloud. Have students repeat the word and then scan the selection to find it. Invite students to explain the word's meaning using context clues and prior knowledge. Then hold a class vote to classify the word by the dinosaur (creature), globe (place), or clock (time). If desired, place the cards and props in a center for individual practice.

2   Sequence of Events

Challenge students to take a closer look at the events described in the selection with this activity. Point out that the author did not present the information in chronological order. Have students locate dates and times in the selection. Discuss possible reasons that the author did not sequence the events. *(The information is arranged to introduce various creatures.)* Follow up by having each student complete the activity on page 35 as directed.

3   Fact and Opinion

This after-reading activity is a "dino-mite" way to help students distinguish fact from opinion! In advance, cut two large dinosaurs from bulletin board paper. Label one "Facts" and the other "Opinions." Also, cut a class supply of three-inch square paper scales from each of two different colors of construction paper. Distribute one scale of each color to each student. Designate one color for facts and one for opinions. Remind students that facts can be proven or observed. Opinions can't be proven and are often based on feelings or beliefs. Direct students to scan the selection and write a fact on one square and an opinion on the other. Then have students share their responses and tape the scales on the corresponding paper dinosaurs.

4   Supporting Details

Invite students to examine the evidence provided in the selection that supports the existence of some living dinosaurs but not others. Begin by asking students how they know crocodiles exist. *(They've read about them or seen them on television.)* List their suggested proofs on the chalkboard. Point out that there is proof that the coelacanth, tuatara, Komodo dragon, and crocodile exist today. On the other hand, no one has been able to prove the present-day existence of the mokele-mbembe or pterosaur. Have students review the selection and explain how the author indicates that the existence of these animals is questionable. Follow up by having each student complete the activity on page 36 as directed.

5   Summarizing

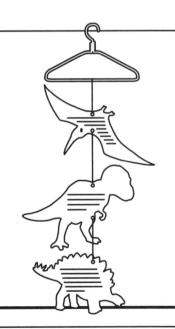

Make a class mobile to give your students practice in summarizing as they examine living dinosaurs. Ahead of time, cut nine large dinosaur shapes from colorful sheets of 9" x 12" construction paper. Divide students into nine groups and assign each group one paragraph from the selection. Give each group one dinosaur shape. Instruct each group to quietly reread its assigned paragraph using choral reading. Have group members identify and underline the paragraph's main idea and two or three supporting details, then work together to summarize the paragraph. Direct one student from the group to write the summary on the dinosaur shape. Provide time for groups to share their work. Then use yarn or string to connect the dinosaurs in order, as shown, to create a mobile that summarizes the entire selection.

Hatching Order

Which came first: the dinosaur or the egg? Perhaps you'll never know. Follow the directions below to learn more about "dinosaurs" that live today.

Directions: An event from the selection is printed on each eggshell. Number each one to show the events in order from past to present. Use the selection to help you.

a. Between 1914 and 1918, a pilot crashes in the ocean and finds Komodo dragons.

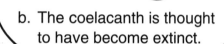

b. The coelacanth is thought to have become extinct.

c. Several schoolteachers claim to see an animal that looks like a pterosaur.

d. Some fishermen catch a coelacanth.

e. The pterosaur flies over the earth more than 65 million years ago.

f. Scientists go to Africa to search for the mokele-mbembe in the 1980s.

g. The distant ancestors of the tuatara die out.

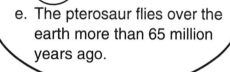

h. Crocodiles lived at the same time as the brontosaurus and tyrannosaurus.

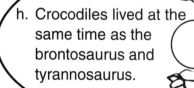

Cool Connection: On the back of this sheet, list five animals mentioned in the selection in order by size from smallest to largest.

Note to the teacher: Use with activity 2 on page 34.

Name_____ *Supporting details*

Spotlight on Living Dinosaurs

C. A. Lizard is producing a special television program called "I'm a Living Dinosaur!" Read the clues below. Match each clue with an animal shown. Write the creature's name on the blank. Then color and cut out each living dinosaur's picture and glue it to the correct spotlight. Use the information in the selection to help you.

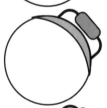
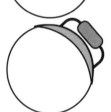

1. I have jagged teeth and long, sharp claws.

_____

2. I survived the Ice Ages and the breakup of the continents.

_____

3. I have three eyes and a bony arch on my skull.

_____

4. Scientists thought I was extinct until I was caught in 1938.

_____

5. Teachers thought they saw me in 1976, but there is no proof that I still exist.

_____

6. I have a huge body and three toes on each foot.

_____

7. I live in the ocean and have silver markings on my pale pink and blue body.

_____

8. My ancient relatives lived at the same time as the tyrannosaurus and brontosaurus.

_____

9. I am the largest living lizard today.

_____

10. Even though some people claim to have seen me in the African Congo, there is no proof that I exist.

_____

11. Today I can be found on several islands near New Zealand.

_____

12. The people who said they saw me in 1976 said I had a 12-foot wingspan.

_____

©The Education Center, Inc. • *Cornerstones of Comprehension* • TEC4104 • Key p. 79

coelacanth   tuatara   Komodo dragon   crocodile   mokele-mbembe   pterosaur

coelacanth   tuatara   Komodo dragon   crocodile   mokele-mbembe   pterosaur

36 **Note to the teacher:** Use with activity 4 on page 34.

If It Only Had a Brain!

A dangerous predator moves smoothly through the water, riding the ocean currents. Sometimes its special pulsing muscle guides it toward its prey or away from its enemies. The creature's strange body may be nearly as clear as glass or beautifully colored. Stringy tentacles dangle from its umbrella-shaped body. Inside those **tentacles** lurk stinging **barbs** like tiny harpoons. The poison in the sting can be deadly. Swimmers spying swarms of these strange creatures dart away in fear. Even if the sting isn't always deadly to humans, it can be painful. It's better to be safe than sorry! In truth, this strange creature isn't out to attack swimmers. It's too much like jelly. It has no eyes, no bones, no heart. It doesn't even have a brain! What is it? A jellyfish!

Jellyfish are not really fish at all. They are **invertebrates.** They have no backbones. Most jellyfish have umbrella-shaped bodies. Their bodies are called *bells.* A jelly's bell has a mouth at its center. Four arms surround its mouth. These arms are called *oral arms.* The jelly uses its oral arms and its tentacles to capture its food. It munches on **plankton,** or tiny plants and animals that float in the water. Some jellies eat fish or even other jellyfish!

Without brains, jellyfish might not have much sense, but they do have **sensors.** Sensors tell a jellyfish where it is. Using their sensors, jellies can smell, taste, and tell light from dark.

Jellyfish can swim using muscles in their bells. These muscles push water out of the bells. This causes the jellyfish to move in the opposite direction. That doesn't mean they're great swimmers. Many jellyfish just drift along in the ocean's *currents.* Currents are movements of water. As the water moves, jellyfish move with it. Jellyfish drift in the water and are called *zooplankton,* or animal drifters.

Jellyfish drift about in oceans all over the world. Some even live in freshwater lakes. They've been around for a long time. Before dinosaurs **roamed** the earth, jellyfish drifted in the seas. They can be up to eight feet in **diameter** with tentacles longer than half a football field. Or they can be about the size of a penny. Jellyfish also come in different colors. But they all have one thing in common: they sting!

Though jellies look like harmless blobs of gel, they are not. The stings on their tentacles and oral arms can stun or kill their **prey.** How dangerous those stings are to humans varies. Some jellyfish stings, such as that of the moon jelly, cause only an itchy rash. Other jellyfish, like the box jelly, are more deadly than cobras! Their stings can kill a human in less than five minutes. Even after they're dead, jellyfish can sometimes still sting.

Despite their deadly stings, jellyfish sometimes become snacks for other animals. Ocean sunfish, leatherback sea turtles, other jellyfish, and even some people think jellies make tasty treats!

Whether they're deadly, itchy, or simply annoying, jellyfish are interesting animals. So the next time you see one, admire its uniqueness—but from a safe distance!

If It Only Had a Brain!

Activities

1 Context Clues

Before students read the selection, explain that readers often figure out unfamiliar word meanings by using context clues, or words or phrases around the unfamiliar word. Ask a student volunteer to read aloud the first sentence in the third paragraph. Point out that some readers might not know the meaning of *sensor*. Continue having the paragraph read aloud. Invite students to identify clues to the meaning of *sensor*. *(Using their sensors, jellies can smell, taste, and tell light from dark.)* Ask a student to define *sensors* based on the clues. *(An organ that responds to light, odor, taste, etc.)* For further practice, have students scan the selection, listing five of the remaining boldfaced vocabulary words. Then have them define each word using context clues.

2 Analogies

After students have read "If It Only Had a Brain!" remind them that an analogy shows a likeness between two objects that are otherwise unlike. Write the following example on the board: meow is to cat as bark is to _____. Guide students to identify the relationship of the word pairs *(sound to object)* and to complete the analogy. Follow up by having each student complete the activity on page 39 as directed.

3 Fact and Opinion

Remind students that facts are based on information that can be observed or checked by using reference material. Opinions are beliefs or feelings that cannot be checked or observed. Ask students to identify which of the following statements is a fact and which is an opinion: Jellyfish are scary. *(opinion)* Jellyfish can be dangerous. *(fact)* Invite students to share several other examples of facts and opinions based on information in the selection. Follow up by having each student complete the activity on page 40 as directed.

4 Summarizing

Summarizing helps students recall what they read. Explain that summarizing a selection is like retelling the important ideas in logical order. Give each student a 9" x 12" sheet of construction paper. Direct her to draw a large jellyfish shape with seven tentacles as shown. Instruct the student to scan the selection and identify the main idea of each of the first seven paragraphs. Then have her write each main idea (in her own words) on a different tentacle. Finally, instruct the student to combine the details into a summary paragraph and write it on the body of the jellyfish. If desired, display the summaries by attaching yarn or string to the jellyfish and hanging them from the ceiling.

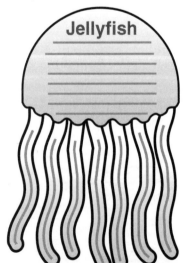
Jellyfish

5 Classifying and Categorizing

After students have read the selection, review classifying information. Direct students to scan the selection and call out the jellyfish-related words, such as *tentacles, moon jelly,* and *bells*. Write the responses on the board. Guide students to sort several of the terms into categories as shown. Then divide the class into groups of three or four, giving each group a sheet of chart paper. Instruct the group to finish classifying the jellyfish terms. If desired, have the group create a unique graphic organizer to display the information.

Types	Body Parts	Predators
moon jelly	tentacles	ocean sunfish
box jelly	oral arms	
	bells	leatherback turtles

Name _____

Jellyfish Analogies

Junior Jellyfish is having trouble describing to his friend Scarlett Scallop how jellyfish compare to other animals. Help Junior by following the directions below to complete the jellyfish analogies.

Directions: Read each analogy below. Think about how the words are related. Write the missing word from the word bank in the space provided. Then explain how the words are related. The first one has been done for you.
Remember: An analogy shows a likeness between two objects that are otherwise unlike.

Analogy

1. Jellyfish is to plankton as cow is to _grass_ .

2. Jellyfish is to float as cheetah is to _____ .

3. Jellyfish is to _____ as starfish is to star.

4. Jellyfish is to sting as cobra is to _____ .

5. Jellyfish is to invertebrate as human is to _____ .

6. Jellyfish is to _____ as monkey is to jungle.

7. Jellyfish is to tentacles as octopus is to _____ .

8. Jellyfish is to _____ as insect is to antennae.

9. Jellyfish is to zooplankton as _____ is to reptile.

10. Jellyfish is to leatherback sea turtle as _____ is to spider.

Explanation

1. Jellyfish eat plankton and cows eat grass.

2. _____

3. _____

4. _____

5. _____

6. _____

7. _____

8. _____

9. _____

10. _____

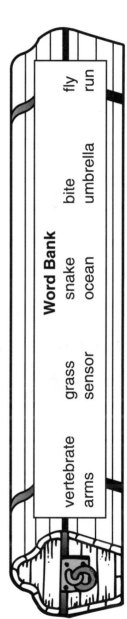

Word Bank

| vertebrate | grass | snake | bite | fly |
| arms | sensor | ocean | umbrella | run |

©The Education Center, Inc. • *Cornerstones of Comprehension* • TEC4104 • Key p. 79

Note to the teacher: Use with activity 2 on page 38.

Name _____ *Fact and opinion*

Jellyfish Facts and Opinions

Have you ever wondered if something you heard was true? If so, remember this: If you can prove something by looking it up in reference materials, then it is a fact. If it is a person's belief or feeling or it can't be looked up, then it is an opinion. Follow the directions below to sort out the jellyfish facts from the opinions.

Directions: Read each jellyfish below. If the statement is a fact, lightly color the jellyfish blue. If the statement is an opinion, lightly color the jellyfish purple.

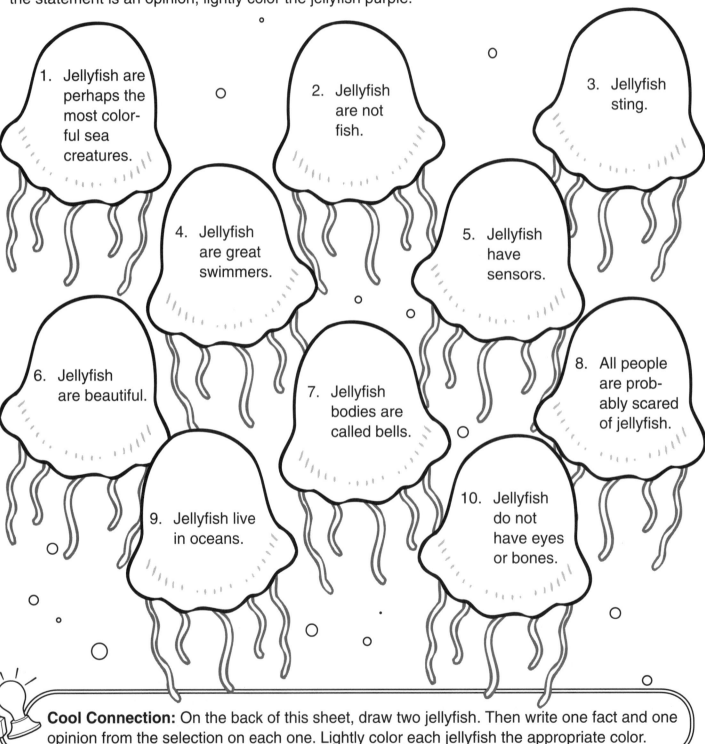

1. Jellyfish are perhaps the most colorful sea creatures.

2. Jellyfish are not fish.

3. Jellyfish sting.

4. Jellyfish are great swimmers.

5. Jellyfish have sensors.

6. Jellyfish are beautiful.

7. Jellyfish bodies are called bells.

8. All people are probably scared of jellyfish.

9. Jellyfish live in oceans.

10. Jellyfish do not have eyes or bones.

Cool Connection: On the back of this sheet, draw two jellyfish. Then write one fact and one opinion from the selection on each one. Lightly color each jellyfish the appropriate color.

©The Education Center, Inc. • *Cornerstones of Comprehension* • TEC4104 • Key p. 79

Spooky Lights in the Night

Some strange sights send shivers up the spine. Spooky lights are enough to give some people goose bumps. People have seen them all over the world. The lights may seem to shine, burn, or glow. They may hum or buzz. There are many legends that try to explain the eerie sights. So far, no one has been able to prove what causes these spooky lights.

Will-o'-the-wisps, also called jack-o'-lanterns, are a kind of spooky light. They are sometimes seen near **marshes** and graveyards. This led to strange beliefs about them. One belief was that the lights were spirits that tricked travelers into getting lost. Others thought that a person who saw the lights would soon die. Is it any wonder that people were afraid of these spooky lights? We still don't know for certain why will-o'-the-wisps appear. Their bluish light may come from the burning of a gas called **methane,** which forms as dead plants **decay.**

Ball lightning is another kind of spooky light. It usually occurs during thunderstorms. Ball lightning can be as small as a pea or as large as a beach ball. It can be blue, yellow, or orange. Ball lightning is very rare and known for the odd way it behaves. Sometimes it floats or glides. Other times it dances or bounces. It can hover or swoop. It may even hum or buzz. So far, no one has been able to prove what causes ball lightning.

Eyewitness stories about ball lightning are amazing. During a storm in 1915 in Missouri, a man saw a bubble of light pop out of his phone. First, the ball of light floated toward him. Then it rolled around near a window just before it vanished. In the summer of 1965, a woman was surprised as ball lightning zipped into her house through her screen door! It was the size of a basketball. She smacked the ball of red-orange light with a flyswatter. When it hit the floor, it exploded with a loud bang.

Ghost lights may be the most mysterious lights of all. Like will-o'-the-wisps and ball lightning, no one really knows what causes them. Some claim that ghost lights are only the reflections of headlights. Others don't agree. After all, **sightings** of ghost lights were reported long before cars were invented. Some ghost lights are quite famous and people travel great distances to see them. There is even a museum **dedicated** to them.

The Spook Light Museum near Joplin, Missouri, is near the Hornet Ghost Light. This spooky light has been seen for more than 100 years. Sometimes it is a ball of light that dims and brightens. It bounces back and forth over the rolling Ozark Mountains. It appears in many colors! People report seeing red, green, blue, yellow, orange, and even gold lights!

Ghost lights near Marfa, Texas, are seen so often that the state has marked an official viewing spot with a sign. When a young **settler** saw them in 1883, he thought they came from **Apache** campfires. People searched for ashes, but none were found. Since that time, many people have seen and tried to explain the lights. So far, there isn't enough proof to support any of the **theories,** and the lights remain a mystery.

Strange lights may seem spooky and send shivers up your spine. While we don't really know why they appear, there probably is a natural explanation. Someday, those who study these strange lights may solve the mystery. Until then, perhaps we should just enjoy the spooky sightings and amusing legends. After all, unsolved mysteries can be fun.

©The Education Center, Inc. • *Cornerstones of Comprehension* • TEC4104

41

Spooky Lights in the Night

Activities

1 Mood

Use this activity to set the mood for reading the selection. Ahead of time, gather three flashlights. To begin the activity, seat students in a large circle and distribute the flashlights to three students. Turn off the classroom lights and invite the students holding the flashlights to turn them on. Then lead a class discussion about the mood created—such as spooky, sleepy, or exciting—by the darkened classroom. Next, have students brainstorm words that they think will describe the mood of the selection. Write the responses on the chalkboard. After reading "Spooky Lights in the Night," review the list and invite students to add additional mood words.

2 Vocabulary

After reading, use this riddle-writing activity to give students practice with the terms used in the selection. To begin, have students use what they learned about one of the spooky phenomena to write a riddle for the class. "Travelers follow my spooky blue light. I'm happy to help you get lost in the night. What am I?" *(Will-o'-the-wisp)* Have students write their riddles on the front of a folded index card and include the answer under the fold. If desired, stack the index cards and punch holes in the top. Then string them onto three-inch loose-leaf rings to create a class riddle book.

3 Supporting Details

Challenge students to recall details about each of the three types of spooky lights with this activity. Ahead of time, write each detail shown below on a separate index card. Give one card to each of three students and invite them to the front of the classroom to take turns reading the details. Instruct the remainder of the students to listen until each detail is read completely. Then have them indicate which is the matching spooky light by giving the correct signal from the list. Follow up by having each student complete the activity on page 43 as directed.

Details

These lights sometimes explode with a loud bang.

People used to believe that these lights were spirits.

This kind of light sometimes seems to dim and brighten.

Signals

Will-o'-the-wisp: shrug and look around as though lost.
Ball lightning: hum quietly.
Ghost lights: say one of the following colors: red, green, blue, yellow, orange, or gold.

4 Fact and Opinion

Students are sure to enjoy this illuminating fact and opinion activity! Point out that *facts* can be observed or proven, while *opinions* show feelings or beliefs and can't be proven. Turn out the classroom lights and give a flashlight to a volunteer. Tell the student to shine it on something in the room and to state a fact or opinion about the lighted object. Then have the student with the light invite a classmate to tell whether the statement was a fact or an opinion. After she answers correctly, invite her to take a turn, shining the light on an object and stating a fact or opinion. Continue the activity until an understanding of fact and opinion is reached. Follow up by having each student complete the activity on page 44 as directed.

5 Summarizing

Remind students that summarizing involves determining important ideas and writing them in one's own words. Direct each student to reread the information in the selection about one type of spooky light. Instruct her to write a brief summary of the information and to copy it neatly on an index card. Next, provide each student with a 12" x 18" sheet of black construction paper, a yellow dot sticker, and access to colored chalk. On the right half of the paper, have the student illustrate the summary using the dot to represent the light and chalk to create the rest of the picture. When she is finished, direct the student to write a story about an imaginary encounter with the spooky light. Have her attach her summary and story to the left of the illustration. Display the completed projects in the classroom.

Spine-Tingling Details

Directions: Read each detail listed below. Decide which kind of spooky light it describes. Then write the number of the detail in the space provided on the matching spooky spine. Use the selection if you need help. The first one has been done for you.

1. sometimes enters houses

2. might be reflections of headlights

3. can be as small as a pea

4. is said to trick travelers into getting lost

5. usually appears during thunderstorms

6. sometimes appears in many colors

Will-o'-the-Wisps

7. sometimes called jack-o'-lanterns

8. might be seen bouncing near the Ozark Mountains

9. known to dance, bounce, hum, and buzz

10. probably caused by burning swamp gas

11. might be viewed from an official spot in Texas

12. sometimes seen in graveyards or marshes

Ball Lightning

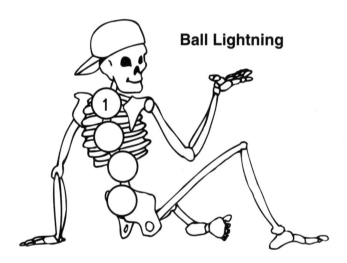

Ghost Lights

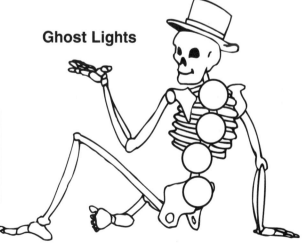

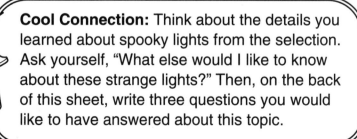

Cool Connection: Think about the details you learned about spooky lights from the selection. Ask yourself, "What else would I like to know about these strange lights?" Then, on the back of this sheet, write three questions you would like to have answered about this topic.

Reporting the Facts

Audrey Author is writing a book about spooky lights based on facts she found in books and articles. She has also talked to eyewitnesses to learn their opinions about strange lights. Last night, she dropped her notes when she was frightened by a ghost light. Help her sort the facts and opinions so she can write her book.

Directions: Read the following statements. If the statement is a fact, check the box on the left. If it is an opinion from an eyewitness, check the box on the right. Remember, a fact can be proven. An opinion is what someone believes to be true.

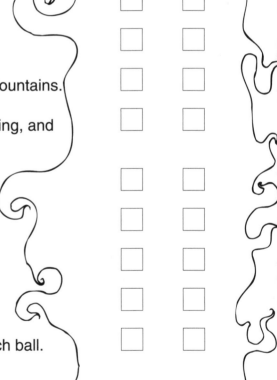

Fact   Opinion

1. Ghost lights are definitely the spookiest lights of all.   ☐ ☐

2. The Spook Light Museum is near Joplin, Missouri.   ☐ ☐

3. Will-o'-the-wisp is a better name than jack-o'-lantern.   ☐ ☐

4. People have reported seeing a ghost light near the Ozark Mountains.   ☐ ☐

5. Three kinds of strange lights are will-o'-the-wisps, ball lightning, and ghost lights.   ☐ ☐

6. Ball lightning is a lot of fun to watch.   ☐ ☐

7. Marsh gases are formed as dead plants decay.   ☐ ☐

8. Will-o'-the-wisps are eerie.   ☐ ☐

9. Ghost lights are scary.   ☐ ☐

10. Ball lightning can be as small as a pea or as large as a beach ball.   ☐ ☐

Cool Connection: Imagine you are a reporter covering the recent sighting of spooky lights near your town. Write a newspaper article about the sighting. Include at least two facts to describe the spooky lights and two opinions from an eyewitness.

Blame It on the Wind

A thick layer of air blankets the earth. As the air warms or cools, it moves from place to place. It causes chimes to ring, sails to fill, kites to soar, and hats to fly off. Air that moves across the earth is called *wind.* It **affects** much of the weather on Earth.

Some say that wind affects more than the weather. They believe it has the power to blow trouble into town. It may sound unlikely, but wind may affect people too. Certain winds seem to carry sickness. Sometimes the crime rate increases when these wild winds blow through town. People may feel tense and upset. Because of these strange effects, some call the **troublesome** winds *witches' winds.*

Where do these witches' winds blow? They blow all over the world! One such wind blows in California. The *Santa Ana* winds begin in the desert. They gain strength as they speed through canyons, then blast hot, dry air into the Los Angeles area. The winds may reach speeds of up to 100 miles per hour. They blow roof tiles off and trucks off highways. They spark fires and fan the flames far and wide. Canyon homes are **destroyed** by fires so large that they can be seen from space. Police often report a rise in **violence** when the winds blow too long. Some say that the name for the winds came from the word *Santana,* which means "devil" wind.

Another fierce wind called the *sirocco* begins as hot, dry air in Northern Africa. It howls across the Mediterranean Sea, picking up **moisture** as it moves along. Then it blows rain and fog into Europe. It is said that crime and sickness in some areas increase while this troublesome wind blows. Judges and doctors notice its harmful effects on criminals and patients.

The mighty *mistral* wind blows cold in France. Its dry breath **spirals** down from the mountains like a funnel. This helps it reach speeds up to 60 miles per hour. When it blows for several days, it can cause crop damage and odd behavior.

Tales about winds that cause sickness or crime might seem **superstitious** or silly. But are they? Researchers have found that dry winds carry lots of positive ions. *Ions* are atoms or molecules that have electric charges. Too many positive ions cause uncomfortable changes in the body. In fact, headaches, pain, chills, and trouble sleeping have been reported by people **exposed** to the ions carried by these winds.

Perhaps people are wrong to believe winds have power to blow trouble their way. Then again, they may be on to something.

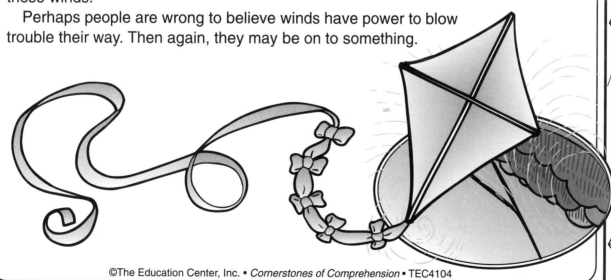

Blame It on the Wind

Activities

1 Classifying and Categorizing

Activate prior knowledge and stir up a storm of ideas about wind with this brainstorming activity. First, divide students into small groups. Provide each group with markers and an 11" x 18" sheet of light-colored paper. Have the group draw and label the graphic organizer as shown. Direct the group to brainstorm ideas to complete the organizer, listing at least three items for each category. Have the groups share their organizers with the class before they read the selection.

2 Main Idea and Supporting Details

Identifying main idea and supporting details will be a breeze with this activity! Pair students and provide each twosome with a 12-inch construction paper kite shape, a 12-inch length of yarn, two construction paper bows, and tape. Assign each pair one of the paragraphs from the selection (except the last one). Direct partners to identify and copy the main idea of their assigned paragraph onto the kite. On the flip side, have partners divide the kite into four sections, writing one supporting detail in each section. Finally, have each student write her name on a bow, tape it to the yarn, and then tape the yarn to the bottom of the kite. If desired, suspend students' kites from the ceiling using lengths of yarn. Follow up by having each student complete the activity on page 47 as directed.

3 Personification

Explain to students that authors use a device called *personification* to give human characteristics to objects that are not human. Then provide each student with a 9" x 12" sheet of white paper. Direct her to draw three equal-sized cartoon panels along the paper's length. Have her write and illustrate a cartoon that features one type of witch's wind. Remind her to use accurate details from the selection about the wind's behavior. Have her include speech bubbles for the wind and other characters. Provide time for students to share their animated adventures with the class. If desired, combine students' pages to create a Witches' Winds booklet for your class library.

4 Synonyms

Remind students that a *synonym* is a word that has the same or nearly the same meaning as another word. Divide students into seven groups, assigning each group one paragraph from the selection. Provide each group with a sheet of chart paper. Have the group reread its assigned paragraph and circle five verbs or adjectives. Then direct group members to brainstorm a synonym for each circled word, using a dictionary or thesaurus for help if needed. Have a recorder rewrite the paragraph on chart paper, substituting the synonyms and underlining them. When the revised paragraphs are complete, invite a member from each group to share its revised paragraph with the class. As the paragraph is read, direct the student to pause after each synonym, allowing the class to chime in with the original word.

5 Similes

Try this activity to help students soar with similes! Remind students that a *simile* compares two things using the words *like* or *as*. Write the following phrase on the board: "Witches' winds are as wild as..." As a class, brainstorm examples of things that are wild, such as a roller coaster ride, fans cheering at a soccer game, or a Tasmanian devil. List the ideas on the board. Next, guide students in connecting the phrase to each listed answer to form similes. Follow up by having each student complete the activity on page 48 as directed.

Blowing in Details

Breeze through your study of main idea and supporting details! Read the main idea shown on each cloud below. Choose two details from the box that support each main idea. Write one on each line. Use the selection to help you.

- It can reach speeds of up to 60 mph and can damage crops.
- Certain winds seem to carry sickness.
- This wind blows rain and fog into Europe.
- Some people seem to get tense or upset.
- Air moves as it warms or cools.
- The winds blast hot, dry air into the Los Angeles area.
- People have reported trouble sleeping.
- They can spark fires that can be seen from space.
- Much of the weather on Earth is affected by the wind.
- When the wind spirals down from the mountains, it moves faster.
- It blows across the Mediterranean Sea, picking up moisture as it moves along.
- Positive ions from these winds can give people headaches, pains, and chills.

1
Air that moves across the earth is called *wind.*

_____
_____

_____
_____

2
Some believe wind has the power to blow trouble into town.

3
The *Santa Ana* winds blow in California.

_____
_____

_____
_____

4
The *sirocco* blows across North Africa.

5
Mistral winds blow in France.

_____
_____

_____
_____

6
Researchers have found that dry winds can cause health-related problems.

Name_____

As Wild As the Wind

Put a new spin on descriptive language using similes! Read the simile shown on each cloud below. Choose a word or phrase at the bottom of the page to complete it. Then cut out the funnel and glue it in the space provided.

1. A thick layer of air covers the earth like a

2. Wind causes objects to soar as high as a

3. The *Santa Ana* winds speed through canyons like a

4. The flames spread as far and wide as a

5. Wild winds may be as deadly as

6. The *sirocco* wind howls across North Africa like a

7. The mighty *mistral* winds blow air as cold as

8. The wind spirals down mountains like a

9. As the strong wind blew, the trucks were tossed around like

©The Education Center, Inc. • *Cornerstones of Comprehension* • TEC4104 • Key p. 80

wolf

ice

toys

funnel

race car

poison

football field

blanket

kite

Note to the teacher: Use with activity 5 on page 46.

The Mysterious Medicine Wheel

Early one morning in 1972, Dr. John Eddy and his family hiked up Medicine Mountain. It was the first day of summer, but ten inches of snow had fallen just days before. Darkness covered them like a blanket as they climbed. Cold air bit their noses. Dampness licked their toes. Still, the family struggled toward the mountain's summit, which was about 9,640 feet above sea level. They would be there before sunrise. Only then would Dr. Eddy be able to learn the secret of the Bighorn Medicine Wheel.

What is a *medicine wheel?* It is a large circle made of stones. More than 50 of these wheels have been discovered in North America. Many were found in Canada. Others were found in the United States. A medicine wheel looks like a big wagon wheel lying flat on the ground. It usually has a central **cairn,** or rock pile. Around the cairn is a circle of stone. **Spokes** made of **cobblestones** lead from the center. Some wheels have small piles of stone at the ends of certain spokes.

Medicine wheels were built by native people long ago. The word *medicine* was used to describe the healers of the tribes. It was thought that a medicine man, or **shaman,** had special powers. His role was to heal the sick and keep contact with the spirit world. A shaman seemed to have strange, powerful magic. The word *medicine* meant "magic" or "mystery." Since the stone wheels seemed mysterious, they became known as medicine wheels.

Medicine wheels are so old that no one remembers how they were first used. Some are thousands of years old. Dr. Eddy wanted to find out why they were built. He was an **astronomer,** a scientist who studies outer space. He was also interested in what **ancient** people knew about the sun, moon, and planets. This interest led him to study the Bighorn Medicine Wheel in 1972. Three or four hundred years before, people built the wheel that is 70 feet across using tons of rock. They must have had a reason. What was it?

Dr. Eddy thought he might have the answer. His idea was that the medicine wheel was a kind of **calendar.** Its builders might have used it to tell when each season began and ended. Dr. Eddy's plan was simple. On the longest day of the year, the summer **solstice,** he would look out from the cairn along one of the wheel's 28 spokes. If the spoke pointed right at the rising sun, it would show that the wheel probably was used to mark the change of seasons.

Ancient peoples used stone calendars to help keep track of the sun's movements. Then they used what they learned to plan the best times to plant and harvest crops. Dr. Eddy thought that the natives of North America probably watched the sky too. If they did, they might have built stone calendars such as those found in other areas of the world.

Dr. Eddy crouched near a cairn on the outer edge of the wheel. Wind had **scoured** it so it was clear of snow. Dr. Eddy peered out along one spoke as the rising sun painted the sky pink. Slowly, it rose like a giant red balloon floating into the sky. There was his answer! The sun was lined up exactly with the cairn at the end of the spoke. The morning was cold, but Dr. Eddy felt warm. He had learned the secret of the mysterious medicine wheel.

The Mysterious Medicine Wheel

Activities

1 Vocabulary

Build students' vocabulary with these mysterious word wheels. Provide each student with a large paper plate, ruler, and dictionary. To help a student create a wheel, instruct him to draw a central circle, use the ruler to draw six spokes around the circle, and number it as shown. Assign one boldfaced word from the reading selection to each student. Direct him to write the word in the circle. Then have him complete each numbered section as follows: write what you know about the word; write the sentence from the selection in which the word is found; write selection clues that help you understand the meaning of the word; write a definition for the word; write the dictionary meaning of the word; and write an original sentence using the word. Finally, group students so that each group has a complete set of vocabulary word wheels. Allow time for each group member to share his new word knowledge.

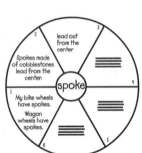

2 Generalizations

Give students practice forming generalizations by combining related facts and details. Before reading the selection, give each student an eight-inch paper circle. Have students fold the circles into quarters and number the sections 1–4. Direct students to read only the selection title. Have each student write in the first section what they think the medicine wheel might be. *(It could be a wheel that spins and dispenses medicine.)* Then instruct students to read the first paragraph and revise their ideas using paragraph details. Have each student write the revision in section two. *(It could be a place where there is strange weather.)* After they read the second and third paragraphs, have each student revise his generalizations again in section three. *(It could be a pattern of rocks where sick people went to get better.)* Finally, after reading the entire selection, have each student use the fourth section to confirm or revise his generalization. *(It is a kind of ancient calendar used to track the seasons.)* Provide time for students to share their responses.

3 Supporting Details

Challenge students to use the details in the selection and their math skills to complete this brain-stretching activity. Begin by directing students to scan the selection to find mathematical details, such as the height of Medicine Mountain and the amount of snow that fell the night Dr. Eddy and his family hiked up to the summit. Then have each student complete the activity on page 51 as directed.

4 Analogies

Take the mystery out of solving analogies with this challenging activity. Explain that an *analogy* shows a likeness between two objects that are otherwise unlike. Give students the following example: "Canada is to North America as France is to Europe." Ask students what the relationship is between the sets of words. *(part to whole)* Brainstorm with students a list of possible relationships, such as synonyms, antonyms, object to description, and object to action. Then have each student complete the activity on page 52 as directed.

5 Descriptive Language

Draw your students' attention to the descriptive language the author uses to give the reader an up-close look at the Bighorn Medicine Wheel. Ahead of time, cut a class supply of large paper circles each into six pizza-shaped slices. Place arts-and-crafts supplies in a central location. To begin, have students close their eyes as you read aloud the first paragraph. Then invite students to describe what they pictured as you read.

Next, divide the class into groups of six students. Assign each group member one of the six remaining paragraphs and provide her with a paper slice. Direct each student to visualize the details as she reads her assigned paragraph silently. Then have the student illustrate the paragraph and label it with selection details that helped her "see" the information. When the illustrations are complete, have each group combine its story slices to form a descriptive circle. Display the circles on a bulletin board titled "The Magic of Descriptive Language."

Supporting details

Mysterious Math

Magic Code Wheel

Are you wondering in which state the Bighorn Medicine Wheel is located? Follow the directions below to discover the answer.

Part 1: Combine information you know with details from the selection to solve each problem.

1. Write this year's date.

   ◯ __ __ __

2. How many years have passed since Dr. John Eddy discovered the secret of the Bighorn Medicine Wheel?

   ◯ __ years

3. Dr. Eddy was 41 years old when he made his discovery on Medicine Mountain. His birthday was on March 25. What year was he born?

   ◯ __ __ __ __

4. According to the selection, about how many medicine wheels have been found in North America?

   ◯ __ medicine wheels

5. One source lists 55 medicine wheels. If 11 of them have been found in the United States, how many have been found in Canada?

   ◯ __ medicine wheels

6. According to the selection, what is the *diameter* (distance across) of the Bighorn Medicine Wheel?

   ◯ __ feet

7. How many spokes does the Bighorn Medicine Wheel have?

   ◯ __ spokes

8. If each spoke is about 36 feet long, what is the total length of all of the spokes?

   ◯ __ __ feet

9. It is thought that the wheel was used by natives from about A.D. 1200 to 1700. For how many years was it used?

   ◯ __ years

Part 2: Look on the code wheel to find the matching letter for each circled number. Then write the letter on the line over the number of the problem.

__ __ __ , __ __ __ __ __ __
6 3 9   1 5 4 2 6 7 8

©The Education Center, Inc. • *Cornerstones of Comprehension* • TEC4104 • Key p. 80

Note to the teacher: Use with activity 3 on page 50.

51

The Mysterious Analogy Wheel

Directions: Read each analogy shown on the wheel. Write the word from the word bank that best completes the analogy. Use the selection or a dictionary if you need help.

Word Bank							
calendar	rising	spoke	lowest	secret	astronomer	powerful	shaman
harvest	summit	early	damp	ancient	circular	sunrise	seasons

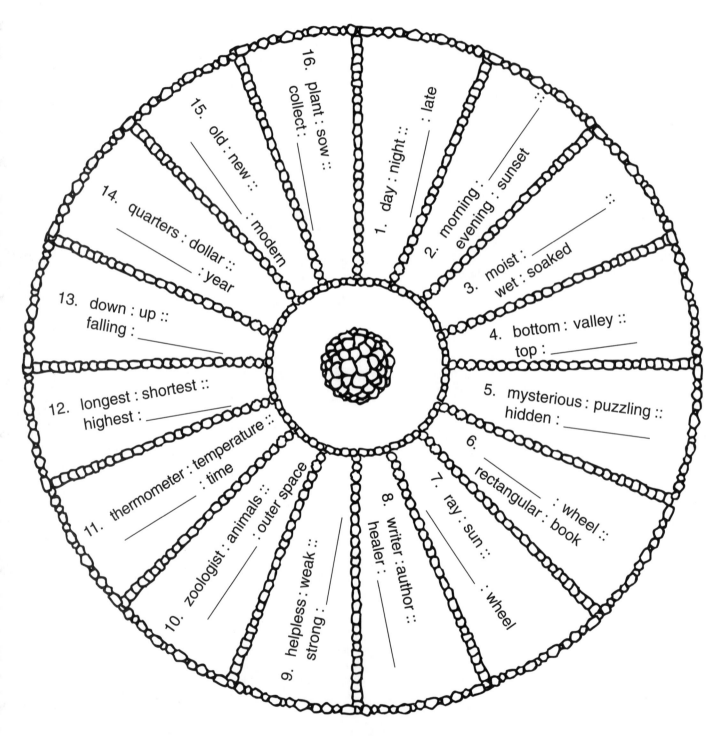

1. day : night :: _____ : late
2. morning : evening :: _____ : sunset
3. moist : _____ :: wet : soaked
4. bottom : valley :: top : _____
5. mysterious : puzzling :: hidden : _____
6. rectangular : book :: _____ : wheel
7. ray : sun :: _____ : wheel
8. writer : author :: healer : _____
9. helpless : weak :: _____ : strong
10. zoologist : animals :: _____ : outer space
11. thermometer : temperature :: _____ : time
12. longest : shortest :: highest : _____
13. down : up :: falling : _____
14. quarters : dollar :: _____ : year
15. old : new :: _____ : modern
16. plant : sow :: _____ : collect

The Island That Rocked the World

It is said that upon waking from a **vivid** dream, a reporter for the *Boston Globe* reached for a pen and paper. His hand may have shaken as he scribbled the details of the dream across the page. A small **island** exploded into the sky. As he wrote, could he picture the explosion and people trying to escape the rain of fire, steam, stone, and ash?

The reporter wrote the story in the form of a news article and called the island Pralape. It was printed on August 29, 1883. When the story was published, the *Boston Globe* did not realize that it was not really a news story. It was later discovered that a **volcano** had **erupted** on an island in the Indian Ocean. But the island was not called Pralape. It was called Krakatau.

Krakatau is a tiny volcanic island in the Indian Ocean. After sleeping for 200 years, the volcano woke with a grouchy rumble. In early 1883, a large **earthquake** rocked the area. In May of the same year, steam and ash rose from the volcano and in August a cloud of black smoke exploded into the sky. People living on nearby islands must have held their breath and watched in fear. The sleeping volcano had turned into a fire-breathing dragon. The force from the volcano's explosions was amazing. Blasts like thunder or cannon fire caused windows to shatter and walls to crack in nearby areas. One could be heard more than 3,000 miles away. Giant ocean waves, moving at great speeds away from the volcano, thundered like freight trains.

On August 27, the dragon erupted again. The huge blast blew away the northern two-thirds of the island. The volcano's cone had risen 6,000 feet above sea level before the explosion. What remained stood only 2,667 feet high. So much ash was thrown into the sky that the area was dark for two and a half days. Giant ocean waves called **tsunamis** crashed over nearby islands. One monster wave swept away more than 160 **coastal** villages, killing more than 36,000 people.

The worldwide effects of the eruption lasted for many years. The volcano coughed dust into the air, blocking some of the sunlight from reaching the earth. Ash buried the islands around it, killing all plant and animal life. Five years went by before living things began to come back. Three months after Krakatau belched steam and ash into the sky, fire engines clanged to life in New York City. Why? Ash from the eruption caused vivid sunsets, which made people think the city was in flames. In Europe it made the sun look green and the moon look blue. Weather around the world changed. **Global** temperatures dropped.

Krakatau slept again until 1927. Then it gave birth to a new volcano. It is called Anak Krakatau, the child of Krakatau. By 1973, the new island had grown to a height of 622 feet. Someday, this baby dragon may become as deadly as its parent. Until then, people living nearby may watch, wait, and worry. Perhaps eruptions haunt their dreams and wake them in the middle of the night.

What about the *Boston Globe* reporter who broke the story back in 1883? Was his dream about the eruption of Pralape just a matter of chance? One would think so. But it was found that 150 years before Krakatau rocked the world, its people had called the island Pralape!

The Island That Rocked the World

Activities

1 Fact and Opinion

This fact-filled account of Krakatau is the perfect spring-board to an easy-to-do fact and opinion activity. Label one sheet of chart paper "Nose for News: Facts Only, Please!" Label another sheet "Your Opinion Counts!" Begin by asking students to skim the story for facts. List these facts on the first chart. Then ask students to suggest opinions they have about the article (for example, "The scariest part was when the tsunamis hit the islands"). As an extension, give each small group of students a newspaper. Have each group compare the front-page stories with those in the editorial section. Ask students, "In which section are facts found? Where would a reader find opinions?"

Nose for News: Facts Only, Please!
- Weather around the world changed.
-

Your Opinion Counts!
- This was a very exciting story!
- The scariest part was when tsunamis hit the islands.
- No one should live near Krakatau today.

2 Analogies

An eruption of analogies will result when you share this activity with students! Give each student a copy of page 55. After discussing with students the information at the top of the page, ask them to suggest other examples of analogies that use synonyms, antonyms, or part-to-whole relation-ships. Then have students complete the page as directed. As an exten-sion, post a simple volcano cutout on a bulletin board. Then have each child write his favorite analogy from the Cool Connection activity on a gray paper cloud. Post the cutouts on the bulletin board along with the title "Analogies Are a Blast!"

Analogies Are a Blast!

3 Sequence of Events

Use this activity to give your students some red-hot practice with sequencing! Divide students into small groups. Give each group a sheet of chart paper and a marker. Have group members work together to list the events of Krakatau's eruption, beginning with the earthquake that took place in 1883. After groups share their lists, discuss as a class any differences in the sequence of events, return-ing to the text to locate supporting evidence as needed. Follow up by having each student complete the activity on page 56 as directed.

4 Metaphors

In "The Island That Rocked the World," the author uses the metaphor of a fire-breathing dragon to describe Krakatau. Help students create their own colorful metaphors using the reproducible on page 57. Give each student a copy of the page. First, work together as a class to read the introduction and complete Part 1. Then have each student complete Part 2 independently as directed. (Or pair students and have each twosome complete Part 2.) Set aside time for students to share their metaphors with the class.

5 Cause and Effect

Krakatau's blast was heard 3,000 miles away, just one of the many effects of the eruption. To practice identifying causes and effects from the selection, draw several simple volcanoes, each on a different sheet of chart paper. Invite students to skim the selection and identify several effects of the eruption. List each effect above a volcano outline using a black marker. Next, have students look at each effect and consider what might happen if it became a cause. Write each new effect on the volcano with a red marker. See the example shown. If desired, post the papers on a wall or bulletin board titled "Krakatau: Far-Reaching Effects."

People in New York think there is a fire.

People may panic.

Businesses may close down.

People may try to leave the city, causing traffic jams.

An Eruption of Analogies

An *analogy* is a way of comparing things. The key to understanding analogies is to identify the relationship between the word pairs. The examples below show five different ways to form analogies. Think about the relationship between the first pair of words. Notice how this helps complete the other word pair.

- *Correct* is to *true* as *incorrect* is to *false.* (synonyms)
- *North* is to *south* as *east* is to *west.* (antonyms)
- *Day* is to *week* as *month* is to *year.* (part to whole)
- *Sun* is to *hot* as *snow* is to *cold.* (object to description)
- *Fish* is to *school* as *member* is to *club.* (member to group)

Directions: Use the information above and the words in the word bank to help you complete each analogy below.

1. *Shore* is to *island* as *tree* is to _____.

2. *Nationwide* is to *national* as *worldwide* is to _____.

3. *Newspaper* is to *sight* as *radio* is to _____.

4. *Nearby* is to *close* as *intense* is to _____.

5. *Real* is to *believable* as *unreal* is to _____.

6. *Truth* is to *lie* as *front* is to _____.

7. *Huge* is to *giant* as *stone* is to _____.

8. *Night* is to *day* as *dark* is to _____.

9. *News* is to *newspaper* as *story* is to _____.

10. *Lava* is to *volcano* as *water* is to _____.

11. *Erupt* is to *explode* as *frightened* is to _____.

12. *Waves* is to *ocean* as *clouds* is to _____.

13. *Adult* is to *grownup* as *anxiety* is to _____.

14. *Sleep* is to *awake* as *fast* is to _____.

15. *Baby* is to *adult* as *puppy* is to _____.

Word Bank

ocean	dog
forest	rock
book	global
vivid	worry
back	scared
slow	sound
sky	light
unbelievable	

Cool Connection: Create three of your own analogies on the back of this sheet. Use a different relationship for each set. Try to use words from the selection in your analogies.

Hot Headlines

Directions: Below are newspaper headlines about an imaginary volcano in the Pacific Ocean named Kiwya. Study the newspaper headlines and decide on their sequence. To help you, use the sequence of events about Krakatau's eruption that you listed earlier. Then rewrite the headlines in order on the blanks. Start with the article that would have been printed first. End with the most recent article at the top. Color in each sun as you use that headline.

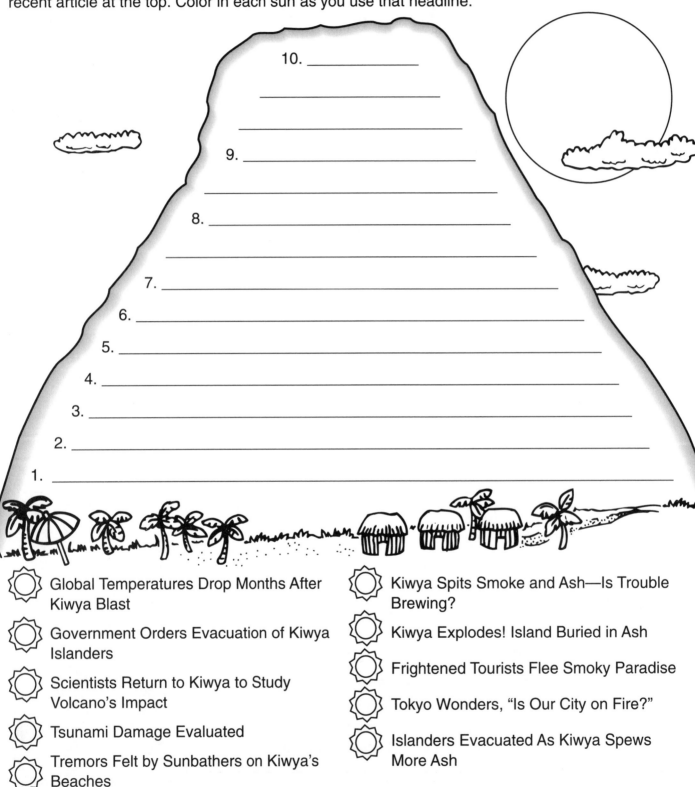

10. _____

_____

_____

9. _____

_____

8. _____

_____

7. _____

6. _____

5. _____

4. _____

3. _____

2. _____

1. _____

Global Temperatures Drop Months After Kiwya Blast

Government Orders Evacuation of Kiwya Islanders

Scientists Return to Kiwya to Study Volcano's Impact

Tsunami Damage Evaluated

Tremors Felt by Sunbathers on Kiwya's Beaches

Kiwya Spits Smoke and Ash—Is Trouble Brewing?

Kiwya Explodes! Island Buried in Ash

Frightened Tourists Flee Smoky Paradise

Tokyo Wonders, "Is Our City on Fire?"

Islanders Evacuated As Kiwya Spews More Ash

Mastering Metaphors

A *metaphor* is a figure of speech that helps a reader visualize the people, places, and things in a piece of writing. Read the two sentences below. Which paints a clearer picture?

No metaphor: The sweater was scratchy.

Metaphor: The <u>sweater</u> was <u>a piece of sandpaper with sleeves</u>.

Part 1: In the selection "The Island That Rocked the World," the author uses a metaphor to describe the volcano. Skim the story to find the metaphor. Write it in the blank.

_____

How was the volcano like the item named in the metaphor?

_____

Part 2: Now it's time to make up your own metaphors! In each box, brainstorm words and ideas about the item listed. On the line below the box, write a metaphor about the item, using one of the ideas in the box.

1. a dream

Brainstorming Box

    The reporter's dream was _____

2. an explosion

Brainstorming Box

    The volcanic explosion was _____

3. darkness

Brainstorming Box

    The darkness after the volcano was _____

4. an earthquake

Brainstorming Box

    The earthquake was _____

Cool Connection: Finish each of these sentence starters to make a metaphor.

1. A tsunami is _____

2. A volcanic island is _____

Keep Your Eyes on the Skies

At first, the people of Woking, England, thought the object was a shooting star. It left behind a glowing, green streak as it sped across the night sky. Sand and gravel were thrown in a wide circle when it slammed into the earth. It was found the next morning, mostly buried in the soft sand of an enormous crater.

News of the crash spread quickly. Folks hurried out to take a look. If it was excitement they were looking for, they were in luck. The object didn't appear to be a **meteorite.** It looked like a huge metal tube. It was still hot and glowing from the trip through the atmosphere. Strange sounds came from somewhere deep inside the tube. Some people began to worry about what it might contain. Very slowly, the giant screw that held the lid began to turn outward. Then the lid fell clanging into the gravel.

No one in the crowd could have guessed what would happen next. A few thought a man would climb out of the dark opening. Instead, two enormous dark eyes peeked over the edge. They were followed by a mass of **writhing** tentacles. One of the many arms gripped the edge of the tube. The creature that **emerged** was about the size of a bear. It was covered in oily, brown skin that shone in the morning light. People screamed and fled in terror.

The story you just read is only one of the countless reports of contact with alien beings from outer space. The **encounter** in Woking, England, did not really take place. It is a story from *The War of the Worlds,* a famous book written in 1898 by H. G. Wells. Later, it was used as the basis of a radio program and a movie.

People seem to enjoy stories about UFOs and have told them for hundreds of years. In A.D. 793, there were reports of lightning bolts and "fiery dragons" in the skies above England. In A.D. 900 a "flying ship" was spotted over Lyon, France. That was long before humans had built any type of flying craft. Today, **television** shows and movies about UFOs and aliens are very popular.

What is a UFO? Is it an alien aircraft? A flying saucer? A *UFO* is simply an **unidentified** flying object. UFOs got the name *flying saucers* in 1947 when an American pilot spotted nine **circular** objects flying near his plane. He said they looked like "saucers skipping over the water." Not all UFOs are round, though. They may be shaped like triangles, squares, cigars, or hats. Some have brightly colored flashing lights. Others seem to glow. They may make sounds or be silent. UFOs seem to be able to travel at great speeds or hover in one place. It seems that there are as many kinds of flying saucers as there are people who report seeing them.

Do flying saucers and aliens really exist? This is the question that **ufologists,** people who study UFOs, are trying to answer. Today the U.S. government doesn't have an official program to study UFOs. Between 1952 and 1969, the Air Force studied sightings through its program called Project Blue Book. They studied more than 12,000 sightings. Of those, only 701 could not be explained. The final report said that UFOs were not a threat and probably did not come from outer space.

No one knows for sure if we live on the only planet with intelligent life. There are billions of stars in space. Some may have planets where life could exist. With SETI, the search for **extraterrestrial** intelligence, researchers listen for radio messages from outer space. Perhaps a message will reach us soon. SETI **astronomers** have also sent a message into space. Maybe it will reach beings far away from Earth. In the meantime, turn your eyes skyward. You might be the next to see something that no one can explain!

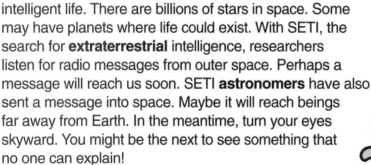

Keep Your Eyes on the Skies

Activities

1 Vocabulary

Before reading the selection, tell students that words can often be understood by understanding the meanings of their individual parts—prefixes, suffixes, and base words. Share the word *interplanetary* with students and have them guess a definition. Next, write each word part and its definition on the board. *(inter = among, between; planetary = of the planets)* Guide students to put the parts together to form a definition. *(something that is among or between the planets)* Next, share the boldfaced words with students, having them guess the meaning of each word by breaking it into parts. Follow up by having each student complete the activity on page 60 as directed.

2 Point of View

"Keep Your Eyes on the Skies" is told in the third person by the narrator. The third-person viewpoint allows the reader to see and know all, but at the same time, it keeps the reader at a distance from the action. After reading the selection, refocus your students' view of the incident described from *The War of the Worlds* and guide them in summarizing the UFO encounter from the first-person point of view. Follow up by having each student complete the activity on page 61 as directed.

3 Cause and Effect

Challenge students to search the selection for unidentified examples of cause and effect. Remind students that an *effect* is what happened and a *cause* is why it happened. Provide each student with a small paper plate, glue, six strips of colored paper, and markers. Instruct her to scan the selection to find six examples of cause and effect. Have the student paraphrase the information in short sentences. For example, "The object slammed into the earth. Sand and gravel were thrown, forming a crater." Direct the student to write the matching cause and effect sentences, each on opposite sides of a paper strip. Have her place a dot of glue at the end of each strip, then glue the strips around the plate as shown. Finally have her decorate the plate to resemble a UFO. Display the UFOs on a bulletin board titled "Close Encounters With Cause and Effect."

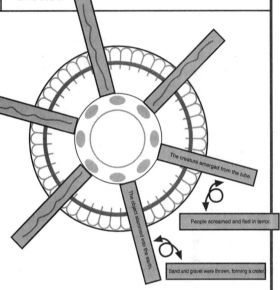

The creature emerged from the tube.

People screamed and fled in terror.

The object slammed into the earth.

Sand and gravel were thrown, forming a crater.

4 Fact and Opinion

Invite your budding ufologists to investigate fact and opinion with this activity. Point out that identifying facts and opinions can be tricky. (Facts can be proven to be true, while opinions cannot.) The first three selection paragraphs appear to be a factual report but turn out to be a story. Divide the class into small groups and provide each group with chart paper and a marker. Direct students to label one side of the chart "Facts" and the other side "Opinions." Instruct students to scan the selection for fact and opinion statements and to list them on the chart in the appropriate columns. When each group has listed several statements, pair groups and direct them to discuss their responses. Encourage students to make changes on their charts based on their discussions. Then post all of the charts and guide a discussion to resolve any disputed statements.

5 Imagery

Have students reread the first three paragraphs of the selection and discuss ways the author creates vivid images that grab the reader's attention. Then invite students to reread the sixth paragraph and discuss ways the details create images of different types of UFOs. Provide each student with a sheet of construction paper and access to crayons, markers, and arts-and-crafts supplies. Have the student create a UFO, based on some of the details found in the selection. When his UFO is complete, direct the student to write a paragraph describing it in detail. Finally, display the UFO projects in the classroom. Have each student read aloud his paragraph and invite the class to identify his UFO from his written description.

Operation Word Watch

You have been asked to take on a special assignment! Read the definitions and word parts below. Match a prefix or suffix on the left file folder to a word or base word on the right file folder to make a new word that matches each definition. Write your new words on the blanks provided. Be sure to spell each word correctly. Use the selection and a dictionary for help.

Example: *en* (in) + *circle* (a closed, curved line with all points the same distance from the center) = *encircle* (to form a circle around)

Prefix/Suffix

- e-: out, away
- en-: in, into
- -er: one who does
- extra-: outside, beyond
- -ing: continuous action
- -ite: mineral or rock
- -ologist: one who studies
- tele-: over a distance
- -ular: relating to
- un-: opposite

Word/Base Word

- astronomy: the study of the planets, stars, and space
- circle: a closed, curved line with all points the same distance from the center
- counter: to come up against or oppose
- identified: recognized as being a certain person or thing
- merged: to plunge in something; immerse
- meteor: a chunk of matter from outer space that enters the earth's atmosphere
- terrestrial: of the earth
- UFO: an unidentified flying object
- vision: the ability to see, the sense of sight
- writhe: to move with twists and turns

1. something not of the earth, but from outer space _____

2. a rock from outer space that enters the earth's atmosphere _____

3. a person who studies the stars, planets, and space _____

4. of or like a circle _____

5. not recognized _____

6. someone who studies unidentified flying objects _____

7. to have come out into view _____

8. an object that receives visual images and the sounds that go with them over a wire or through space _____

9. to come into contact or meet face-to-face _____

10. moving about with twists and turns _____

©The Education Center, Inc. • *Cornerstones of Comprehension* • TEC4104 • Key p. 80

Note to the teacher: Use with activity 1 on page 59.

Close Encounters!

Directions: Pretend that you were in Woking, England, on the night of the alien encounter. As a result, special agents have asked you to complete a report. Use information from the selection and your imagination to complete the report, including what you saw, heard, and felt. Be sure to write your report in the first person. For example, "I saw what looked like a shooting star…."

Name: _____

Date and time of sighting: _____

Description of alien: _____

_____

_____

_____

Description of encounter (what you saw, heard, and felt happening):

_____

_____

_____

_____

_____

_____

_____

_____

_____

_____

Your signature

Draw picture here.

Note to the teacher: Use with activity 2 on page 59.

Winged Thunder

Marlon Lowe pumped his legs as hard as he could. His heart knocked in his chest as he ran. His friend Travis had fled toward the swimming pool. Marlon heard a splash as Travis **hurled** himself into the water. No matter how fast Marlon ran, he could not stay ahead of the black shape that **loomed** over him. Then claws gripped his shoulders, tugging upward. There was nothing he could do. One of the giant black birds that had **swooped** into his backyard lifted him and carried him into the sky.

Marlon, now **frantic,** shouted and punched at the bird. Far below, he saw his mom and dad. They froze like statues and stared in horror as the bird lifted their son higher and higher. Marlon kept punching the beast's legs as hard as he could. Suddenly, the bird opened its **talons.** The boy landed with a thud.

Marlon's parents said that the bird looked something like an Andean **condor.** This bird is a giant, black **vulture** with a **wingspan** of up to ten feet. The Andean condor doesn't live in North America. It lives miles away in South America. It is extremely **rare,** even in its natural **habitat.** It is not able to lift something as heavy as a ten-year-old boy. Perhaps the bird that tried to **kidnap** Marlon was not a condor at all. Perhaps it was a bird believed to exist only in legends—the Thunderbird.

A number of Native American tribes have told tales of the Thunderbird. To the Winnebago people of the northern Midwest and Plains states, it was a powerful bird like an eagle. It could create storms, causing lightning to strike and thunder to boom. To the Passamaquoddy people of Maine, it was a man who could turn into a flying creature. It too had power over winds and storms. The Quillayute people living near Seattle, Washington, feared the powerful Thunderbird. Its eyes glowed like fire. When it flapped its wings, thunder boomed. When it opened and shut its eyes, lightning flashed. Could this **legendary** bird have been the one that scooped up Marlon Lowe?

Through the years, there have been reports of the **fearsome** Thunderbird. In 1890, a newspaper story told of two cowboys who had seen a bird that was 92 feet long and had a 160-foot wingspan. The cowboys had shot it and brought its body back to town. Since that would make the bird about the size of an airplane, it seems clear that the story was a tall tale. But in 1970, a man named Harry McClure said that he had met the cowboys as a boy. They had told him a different story. They said that the bird really had a wingspan of about 20 feet. They shot at the bird, but it flew away. That may have been a good thing. Even a 20-foot bird would be more than two cowboys could **tote** home from the range!

Another sighting took place in 1977. An Illinois farmer and his wife were watching some people flying model planes. One of the planes turned out to be a giant bird. In fact, its body was the size of a man and its wingspan was ten feet. The bird had a hooked beak. It had a white ring around its neck. There were many others who saw this bird as well. It also looked like an Andean condor.

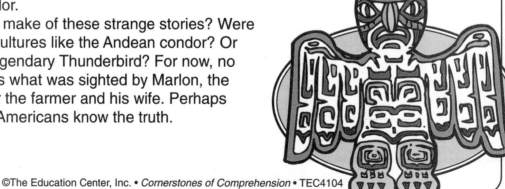

What can we make of these strange stories? Were the birds huge vultures like the Andean condor? Or were they the legendary Thunderbird? For now, no one really knows what was sighted by Marlon, the two cowboys, or the farmer and his wife. Perhaps only the Native Americans know the truth.

Winged Thunder

Activities

1   Drawing Conclusions

Before reading, explain that part of the selection is about a legend, or a story about a real event or person that has been exaggerated. To demonstrate, whisper this excerpt to a student: "In 1890, a newspaper story told of two cowboys who had seen a bird that was 92 feet long and had a 160-foot wingspan." Direct that student to whisper the information to a nearby classmate and so on until each student has heard it. As the last child whispers the information back to you, write it on the board. Discuss any changes in the information and guide students to conclude that stories can be changed or exaggerated as they are retold. After reading the selection, have each student complete the activity on page 64 as directed.

2   Vocabulary

"Winged Thunder" includes several words that may be unfamiliar to students. Remind students that they can use the other words in a sentence (known as the word's *context*) to determine each new word's meaning. Point out that they should not only study the sentence that includes the word, but also the sentences that come before and after it. Also encourage students to look for clues that identify the unknown word's part of speech. Follow up by having each student complete the activity on page 65 as directed.

3   Judgments

When faced with fantastic accounts or legends like those told in this selection, readers must make judgments about what is believable. To help students do that, list titles for the different accounts on the board, such as "Marlon Lowe's Account" or "1977 Sightings." Discuss which ones seem convincing. Then have each student write her name beside the account or legend she thinks is most believable. Ask volunteers to explain their votes. Then have each student create an illustration of the legend on a sheet of drawing paper. Beneath the picture, have the student write a paragraph in which she explains the reasons for her choice.

Winnebago Legend

4   Comparing and Contrasting

Use details from the various Thunderbird legends found in this selection to help students practice comparing and contrasting. Have each student fold a sheet of paper into thirds. Instruct him to label the first column "Winnebago," the middle column "Passamaquoddy," and the final column "Quillayute." Then have the student use the top half of each column to compare similarities among the people's beliefs about the Thunderbird. Direct him to contrast those beliefs on the bottom half of the paper. Provide time for students to share their findings.

Winnebago	Passama- quoddy	Quillayute

5   Summarizing

Build summarizing skills with this easy-to-do activity. First, ask students to identify the topic of the selection (fearsome birds). Then have each student write "FEARSOME BIRDS" down the left side of her paper as shown. Beside each letter, have the student write a word or phrase beginning with that letter that describes an aspect of the Thunderbird or the legends about it. When students are finished, have each child use her list to help her write a brief summary of the selection. Provide time for students to share their finished summaries.

F lying creatures
E xtremely large
A ncient legend
R esemble condors
S harp talons
O
M
E

B
I
R
D
S

Name _____

Thunderbird Theory

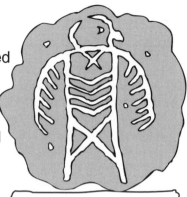

As legends get passed down from generation to generation, they have a tendency to grow and grow and grow. Could this have happened with the legendary Thunderbird?

Directions: Perhaps the legend of the Thunderbird started with an actual bird that later became exaggerated. Think about what the actual Thunderbird might have been like. Then answer the questions below. Be sure to support your answers using details from the selection.

1. What might the actual Thunderbird have looked like before generations had the chance to exaggerate it? _____

_____

_____

_____

_____

2. What might the actual Thunderbird have been able to do? _____

_____

_____

_____

_____

_____

3. Why do you think stories sometimes become exaggerated the longer they are told?

_____

_____

_____

_____

_____

Cool Connection: Have you ever told a story to a friend or family member that might have been exaggerated? What was the story? What did you exaggerate and why? Write your explanation on the back of this sheet.

Note to the teacher: Use with activity 1 on page 63.

Name _____   *Vocabulary*

Winged Words

You don't have to wing it when it comes to figuring out new vocabulary words! Just use the context clues surrounding the word you don't know.

Directions: Read each statement below. Then reread the sentence from the selection that includes the boldfaced word. Decide if the statement is true or false. Color the thunderbird that shows your decision.

		True	False
1.	If Travis **hurled** himself into the pool, he threw himself in.	D	M
2.	**Loomed** means "to shake violently."	A	O
3.	**Swooped** means "to scream loudly."	E	I
4.	The Thunderbird's **talons** are its claws.	A	C
5.	A **condor** is a type of bird.	N	F
6.	A **vulture** is a small songbird.	G	S
7.	A bird's **wingspan** is the distance from the tip of one wing to the tip of the other wing.	E	A
8.	Something that is **rare** is easy to find.	T	M
9.	An animal's **habitat** is the place where it lives and grows.	S	U
10.	To **kidnap** a person is to take him or her away by force.	A	L
11.	**Legendary** means "brightly colored."	R	N
12.	If someone is **frantic,** he is calm and not worried.	B	N
13.	A **fearsome** person or creature is very afraid.	Y	U
14.	**Tote** means the same thing as *carry*.	T	D

Cool Connection: The Thunderbird is said to look like the Andean condor. What place does *Andean* refer to? To find out, write the letter that you colored for each number shown below.

The __ __ __ __ __   __ __ __ __ __ __ __ __ __ in South America
    4 12 1 7 9   8 2 13 5 14 10 3 11 6

©The Education Center, Inc. • *Cornerstones of Comprehension* • TEC4104 • Key p. 80

Note to the teacher: Use with activity 2 on page 63.

65

Ship of Dreams

Deep beneath the icy waters of the Atlantic, dishes, shoes, coins, and jewels litter the ocean floor. Twisted metal rots in the salty water. These are the remains of a giant passenger ship that plunged 12,460 feet to its watery grave.

Her name was *Titanic.* She was four city blocks long and 11 stories high. She was like a grand lady, decked out in sparkling crystal and polished wood. Her grand staircase was crowned with a glass dome that invited sunlight into the ship. *Titanic* boasted a swimming pool, **gymnasium,** and fancy restaurants. Her guests included men, women, and children. Some were wealthy and famous. Many more were poor, on their way to America to begin new lives. She was a ship of dreams.

On the night of April 14, 1912, the dream became a nightmare. After dinner, men played cards. Women listened to music and chatted together. Some passengers went to parties. Around 10:00, people began to drift off to bed.

Outside, it was bitter cold. High above the deck in the **crow's nest,** two men scanned the **horizon** for signs of ice. Stars twinkled in the moonless sky. The sea was calm and smooth as glass. From his frozen perch, one lookout suddenly spotted a mountain of ice.

"Iceberg right ahead!" he shouted through the phone to the bridge.

The First Officer sprang into action. He called for the engines to be stopped and thrown into reverse. He gave orders to turn the ship hard to **starboard.** It was too late. There was a bump and grinding noise as giant claws of ice scraped the side of the ship.

Titanic's double-bottom **hull** was divided into 16 sections. Even if four of the front sections flooded, the ship would still float. But the icy monster had cut gashes along six sections. Freezing cold water flooded one section after another. *Titanic* was doomed.

Distress messages were sent by radio in the hope that a passing ship would come to help. Meanwhile, **stewards** began to **rouse** sleeping passengers. The passengers put on life jackets and gathered on deck. The ship's orchestra played cheerful music to help keep people calm. Orders were given for women and children to get into the lifeboats. Some of the passengers wanted to stay on the warm, comfortable ship. They were afraid to trust their lives to the tiny boats dangling above the frigid sea.

To make matters worse, *Titanic* carried only enough lifeboats for 1,178 of the 2,207 people aboard. Officers worked to load the boats, but they were afraid to put too many people in one boat. Many were launched only half filled. One boat, made for 65 people, left with just 19. As the lifeboats rowed away, the ship began to sink. People left behind may have fled to the ship's **stern** as the **bow** dipped into the water.

The shivering survivors watched helplessly from the lifeboats as the ship tilted. Its lights still twinkled like stars in the clear night sky. Awful sounds came from the wounded ship. Furniture, plates, glasses, luggage, and everything else on the ship broke loose with a sound like thunder. Then *Titanic* broke in two with a groan. The lights went out. *Titanic* paused for two minutes before sinking out of sight. Hours later, a ship called the *Carpathia* came to the rescue. The 705 survivors were given hot food and blankets. Three and a half days later, they arrived in New York.

Many years passed before the remains of the ship of dreams were found. The crow's nest bell, toys, shoes, coins, and other objects are grim reminders of the tragedy. Now the grand lady's only guests are the few sea creatures that live in the icy depths.

TITANIC

Ship of Dreams

Activities

1   Vocabulary

Before reading the selection, steer students through an exploration of vocabulary with this activity. Draw a large life preserver on bulletin board paper. Cut out the shape, use a marker to divide it into ten sections, and then post it at the front of the classroom. Label each section with one boldfaced word. Then, in turn, invite students to share prior knowledge of each word's meaning. (For unknown words, have students locate the definitions in a dictionary.) Add each definition to the chart as shown. After discussing each word's meaning, ask a student to make up a sentence using the word. Add students' responses to the chart. Follow up by providing each student with scissors and glue. Have each student complete the activity on page 68 as directed.

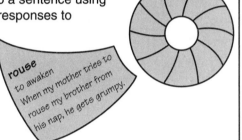

rouse
to awaken
When my mother tries to rouse my brother from his nap, he gets grumpy.

2   Paraphrasing

Paraphrasing is a great way to check for understanding. Ahead of time, write a paraphrased version of the selection's first paragraph on a sheet of chart paper. *(The remains of a huge passenger ship lay deep in the Atlantic Ocean.)* Ask a student to read the first paragraph of the selection aloud. Then have a different student read the paraphrased version aloud. Discuss how it is different. (It includes a main idea and fewer details.) Continue reading aloud and paraphrasing remaining paragraphs. Follow up by having each student complete the activity on page 69 as directed.

3   Synonyms

Get students ready for smooth sailing through a sea of synonyms! To begin, list the following words on the chalkboard: *famous, boasted, poor, wealthy,* and *afraid.* Remind students that a synonym is a word with the same or nearly the same meaning as another word. Ask students to identify synonyms for each of the listed words using a dictionary or thesaurus, if necessary. Write the responses on the chalkboard and take a few minutes to discuss the word meanings. Then provide each student with scissors and glue. Follow up by having each student complete the activity on page 70 as directed.

4   Judgments

Invite students to imagine that *Titanic*'s survivors blame the White Star Line, the company that owned the ship, for the tragedy. Explain that deciding whether an action is right or wrong is making a *judgment.* It is *valid* if it is supported by facts and evidence. Divide the class into groups of three. Assign the following roles: court recorder, court officer, and judge. Provide each group with a large sheet of paper. Direct the judge to decide if the White Star Line is to blame. Then instruct group members to reread the selection and decide if the judge's decision is valid. Then have them cite evidence supporting their decision. Have the court recorder write the judgment and evidence on the paper. When the groups have finished citing evidence, invite each court officer to present her group's verdict to the class.

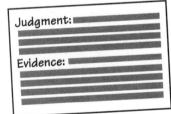

5   Descriptive Language

Explain to students that authors use descriptive words to paint vivid pictures about the details in a story. As a class, have students scan the selection for descriptive phrases and read them aloud. Then provide each student with an 11" x 14" sheet of black construction paper and access to construction paper of various colors. Guide each student in using the colored paper to create a nighttime scene of the *Titanic* as shown. Then have her copy descriptive sentences from the selection on slips of paper and glue each one to an appropriate location on her picture. Provide time for students to share their projects with the class.

Vocabulary Voyage

Preserve your understanding of vocabulary found in "Ship of Dreams".

Directions: Cut out the circles at the bottom of the page. Match each word on a circle to a definition shown on a life preserver. Use context clues from the selection or a dictionary if you need help. Once all words have been matched, glue them in place.

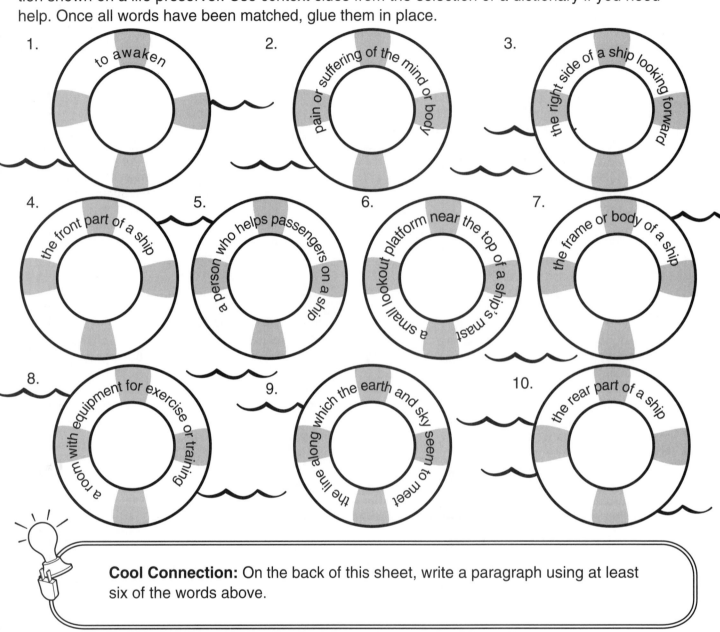

1. to awaken
2. pain or suffering of the mind or body
3. the right side of a ship looking forward
4. the front part of a ship
5. a person who helps passengers on a ship
6. a small lookout platform near the top of a ship's mast
7. the frame or body of a ship
8. a room with equipment for exercise or training
9. the line along which the earth and sky seem to meet
10. the rear part of a ship

Cool Connection: On the back of this sheet, write a paragraph using at least six of the words above.

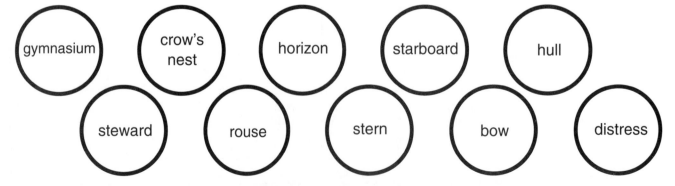

gymnasium crow's nest horizon starboard hull

steward rouse stern bow distress

Note to the teacher: Use with activity 1 on page 67.

Name _____

Paraphrasing

Titanic Telegrams

Imagine that you are a reporter aboard the *Titanic*. Each sentence below includes too much detail to be sent by telegram. Follow the directions to send a series of shorter messages to your newspaper office.

Directions: Paraphrase each of the sentences on the lines provided using as few words as possible. Be sure to capture the main idea of the original sentence. Then count the words and calculate the cost of each telegram.

1. From their frozen perch in the crow's nest, two lookouts scanned the dark, glassy sea for icebergs that might be lurking ahead of the ship.

To: Daily Globe	Date: April 14, 1912

$3.00 + ($.35 x _____ for words over 10)

2. By the time the First Officer gave his orders for the engines to be stopped and for the ship to be turned, it was too late to avoid crashing into the mountain of ice.

To: Daily Globe	Date: April 14, 1912

$3.00 + ($.35 x _____ for words over 10)

3. Freezing cold water flooded into six sections of the double-bottom hull of the great ship.

To: Daily Globe	Date: April 14, 1912

$3.00 + ($.35 x _____ for words over 10)

4. Even though the plan for *Titanic* called for 64 lifeboats, which was enough for 2,207 passengers, the builders only placed the required number of 16 on the ship.

To: Daily Globe	Date: April 14, 1912

$3.00 + ($.35 x _____ for words over 10)

5. When the lifeboats were gone and *Titanic's* bow began to dip deeper into the icy water, people who were still on board may have fled back toward the stern of the ship.

To: Daily Globe	Date: April 14, 1912

$3.00 + ($.35 x _____ for words over 10)

6. The shivering people in the lifeboats watched helplessly as the lights went out and the huge ship sank out of sight.

To: Daily Globe	Date: April 14, 1912

$3.00 + ($.35 x _____ for words over 10)

©The Education Center, Inc. • *Cornerstones of Comprehension* • TEC4104 • Key p. 80

Note to the teacher: Use with activity 2 on page 67.

69

Sailing the Synonym Sea

Follow the directions below for smooth sailing through the sea of synonyms.

Directions: Cut out the diamond shapes at the bottom of the page. Find the two triangles on the sail that show synonyms for each word on the diamond. Cover the two triangles with the matching word cutout. *(Hint: You may have to turn the cutout to make it fit.)* After all the cutouts have been arranged, place a drop of glue at the tip of each diamond to secure it. After the diamonds dry, flip up each one to review the synonyms.

C
yell

F shiny A awaken P
glossy I talk N stir

L stroll Z drop F chilly G
flat I fall M crowd W freezing

E tremble A still O terrible O empty M
shake P quiet I firm N horrible R glitter

S huge N lost L suspend A slash S sparkle N
magnificent A crooked I hang W warm E cut G save

Discover the name of the ship that tried to warn *Titanic* of icebergs before the accident. Write the remaining letters in order on the lines below.

_____ _____ _____ _____ _____ _____ _____

grand   polished   plunge   twinkle   calm   gash

rouse   dangle   frigid   shiver   grim

Note to the teacher: Use with activity 3 on page 67.

Riding the Long Island Express

Arthur Raynor, like others living on Long Island, New York, rested easy on the morning of September 21, 1938. Weather **forecasters** said a **hurricane** was headed toward Florida, but that was far away. Besides, no hurricane had hit Long Island for over 100 years. Around lunchtime, Arthur stood at a window, staring at a flock of birds. He thought they were acting pretty goofy. He'd just seen a movie called *Typhoon* at the local theater. The birds in the movie had acted strange before the typhoon hit. Maybe the goofy birds meant bad weather was coming. His grandmother shook her head as she explained that folks living on Long Island didn't have to worry about hurricanes.

Arthur wasn't about to argue with his grandmother. Besides, he and his friend John were about to head out for some fun. "Be careful!" his grandmother called as he headed out the door.

It was a gray, rainy day. That was nothing unusual for fall in Long Island. Cold, nasty **squalls** blew in all the time but never did much more than break a branch off someone's tree. Arthur jumped into John's 1929 Chevy. They picked up another friend, Lillian. Then the three teens headed for an afternoon of indoor skating. As they got out of the car, wind gusted around them. The manager **informed** them that there would be no skating that day and pointed toward the roof. Part of it had blown off. Water puddled beneath the gaping hole.

They piled back into the Chevy and drove down East Main Street, hoping to see a movie. Much to their surprise, they found a parking spot right in front of the theater. It seemed to be their lucky day! Their luck was about to change. As they stood in front of the theater, light flashed and a loud noise buzzed from a power pole across the street. A broken power line swung in the wind. Down the street, the roof of the hardware store ripped off and landed on some cars.

The trio again jumped into John's car and started to head home. As they drove, they decided to take a **detour** toward the beach. They thought the waves must be huge!

Before reaching the beach, they stopped at the **yachting** area. What they saw sent chills through them! The ocean **plowed** through the West Bay Bathing Club. The end of the bridge seemed to be standing straight up!

This was no ordinary storm. It had turned deadly. The drive home was a blur of falling trees, pounding wind, and rushing water. Arthur thought of his grandfather out on the **bay** in his small fishing boat. He'd gone out to check his **eel** pots that morning. The small boat couldn't possibly **survive** such a storm. He might never see his grandfather again. He knew he had to get back to the house and his grandmother.

At last, Arthur rushed into the house. When he reached the kitchen, he could not believe his eyes. His grandfather stood at the sink, calmly washing his face and hands. He had survived the storm. Both of his grandparents were safe. All was well!

Though Arthur and his grandparents were safe, the hurricane that roared through Long Island was a killer, just as Arthur feared. If he and his friends had made it to the beach, they could have been swept away. A 40-foot-high wave slammed into the beach when the hurricane hit. At least 600 people died that day. The hurricane destroyed over 57,000 homes. It **toppled** millions of trees. Arthur and his grandparents were lucky indeed that the hurricane known as the "Long Island Express" **spared** their lives.

Riding the Long Island Express

Activities

1 Predictions

Is a title a good predictor of what a story will be about? Not always, as your students will see with this drawing activity. Write the title "Riding the Long Island Express" on the board. Give each student a sheet of drawing paper. Direct the student to draw a quick sketch on the left side of the paper, showing what she predicts the selection will be about based on the title. After reading the passage, instruct each student to draw a second sketch on the right side of the paper, showing what the story was actually about. Ask your students if they believe that titles are always good predictors of content, using their drawings to help explain their reasonings.

2 Vocabulary

Stir up a storm of knowledge with this vocabulary activity! Begin by drawing a graphic organizer and labeling it with the boldfaced words from the selection as shown. Ask students what they know about each word. Next, write "storm" on the center circle of the organizer, explaining that this is the topic of the selection. Have students skim the selection and share the sentences surrounding each boldfaced word. Based on the information gained from the selection, have students add or change the information about each word's meaning, guiding them to include how each word is related to the topic. Record their responses around the organizer. Follow up by having each student complete the activity on page 73 as directed.

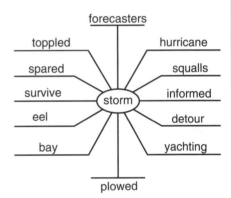

3 Mood

Make mood the focus of this whole-class activity. Begin a class discussion about the mood of the story, highlighting two of the contrasting moods *(apprehensiveness* and *calm)*. Explain the meaning of each mood. Then, for each mood, choose an action for students to imitate that represents it. For example, stand up stiffly *(apprehensiveness)* and then rest your head on the back of your hand *(calm)*. Ask student volunteers to read the story aloud, stopping briefly after each paragraph. Have the rest of the class respond to each paragraph by imitating the action for the mood that is produced by the paragraph. Tally students' actions on the board. Summarize the story's mood by counting the tally marks and discussing the totals.

4 Relevant and Irrelevant Details

Helping your students understand important story details is a breeze with this whole-class activity! In advance, cut out a class supply of colored tissue paper squares. Begin the activity by discussing the difference between relevant and irrelevant details. Next, have each student use a ballpoint pen or fine-tipped marker to write a sentence from the selection on his square. Then direct students to sit in a circle on the floor. On your count have each student blow his sentence toward the center of the circle. Then, one at a time, instruct each student to select a square to read aloud. Have the rest of the class decide whether the sentence is a relevant or irrelevant detail and explain why.

> Besides, no hurricane had hit Long Island for over 100 years.

> As they drove, they decided to take a detour toward the beach.

5 Climax

Step up your students' sequencing skills as they construct a story ladder based on the selection. Discuss with students *climax,* the point of highest tension or where something must happen in a story. Talk about the highest point in "Riding the Long Island Express" *(when Arthur rushes back to his grandmother's house)*. Then have students point out which events helped guide them to realize that something was about to happen. Follow up by having each student complete the activity on page 74 as directed.

Word Wisdom

Part 1: Complete each sentence in the organizer below using a boldfaced word from the selection. Use clues in each sentence to help you. Then use the codes shown to tell more about each word: Color each section to show the word's part of speech and draw a symbol in the box to show its number of syllables.

Part of Speech	
red = noun	purple = verb

Number of Syllables
☆ = 1   ◯ = 2   △ = 3

1. I thought I saw a snake slithering through the water, but my dad told me it was an _____.

2. As we headed out to sea in our boat, we turned and watched the fish jump from the beautiful _____.

3. We were told to evacuate the area as a very powerful _____ with winds over 75 mph was headed our way.

4. My friend Frank listened carefully as the _____ detailed the predicted wind speed and rainfall of the upcoming storm.

5. Grandmother _____ us that we should put on proper weather gear before heading outside.

6. Fall _____ come on quickly, bringing downpours of rain.

7. Even though I had not been _____ before, I had sailed on a small boat.

8. A surprising storm caused our neighbors to lose two trees, but our yard was _____.

9. We didn't think we would _____ the effects of the wind and rain!

10. The old tree _____ during the storm because its trunk was too weak and thin to support its massive branches.

11. My little brother _____ through puddles of water after the storm.

12. The road was flooded with water, so we had to take a _____.

Part 2: Imagine that you are a news reporter for a newspaper called the *Long Island Ledger.* On the back of this sheet, write a report detailing an account of a recent storm. Use as many of the words above as possible. Write the number of words you used in the storm symbol at the right and then use the code to determine your score!

12 = You blow me away!   **10–11 =** You are a super storm chaser!
8–9 = You've got a tornado of talent!

Note to the teacher: Use with activity 2 on page 72.

Name_____

Climax

The Excitement Is Rising

The excitement is rising with this climax activity! The *climax* of a reading selection is the point of highest tension or the point where something must happen. Follow the directions below to learn more.

Directions: Read the ten events listed at the bottom of the page. Cut out the events, and then arrange them in the order in which they occurred. Beginning with the first event as number one, glue each event in order, building to the climax of the story.

Climax!
Arthur's grandparents are safe—all is well!

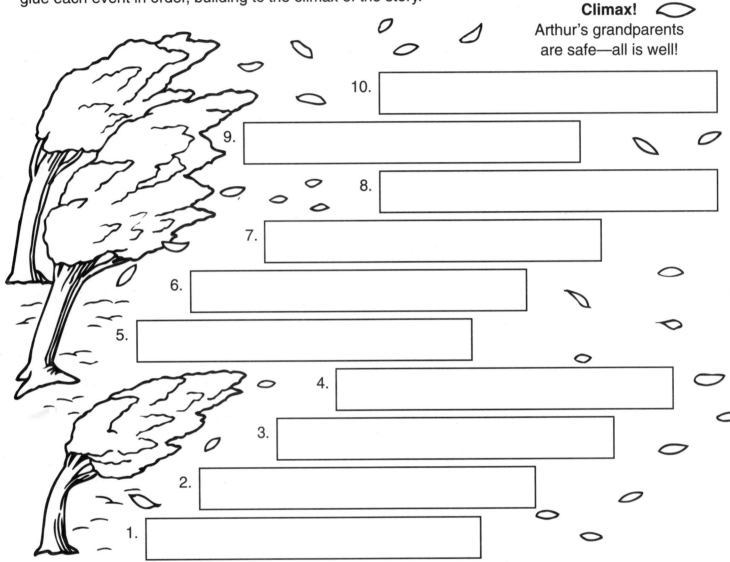

10.

9.

8.

7.

6.

5.

4.

3.

2.

1.

©The Education Center, Inc. • *Cornerstones of Comprehension* • TEC4104 • Key p. 80

Skating is canceled because part of the roof has blown off.	It is a gray, rainy day.
A flock of birds is acting goofy.	Arthur thinks about his grandfather out on the bay in his small fishing boat.
Arthur desperately wants to get home.	A power line breaks and swings in the wind.
They drive through pounding wind and past falling trees and rushing water.	Arthur rushes into the house.
The roof of the hardware store rips off.	The ocean plows through the West Bay Bathing Club.

74   **Note to the teacher:** Use with activity 5 on page 72.

Lady Lindy and the First Lady

Amelia Earhart was a tall, slim **tomboy** of a girl. Growing up in the early 1900s, Amelia dared to do what other girls didn't. She climbed trees. She played baseball. She **bolted** down snowy hills on her sled. She even built a roller coaster in her backyard! Riding the roller coaster made her feel as if she were flying.

Eleanor Roosevelt's childhood wasn't like Amelia's. Eleanor was shy and **awkward.** She was so serious that her mother called her Granny. Eleanor spent much of her time alone. She read a lot and played the piano. She learned to sew and **embroider.** She studied French and German.

Amelia and Eleanor had very different childhoods, but both grew up to do amazing things. Amelia became a pilot. She was one of a few women pilots of her time. She was the first woman to fly **solo** across the Atlantic Ocean. Charles Lindbergh had been the first man to do so. Since Amelia looked so much like Lindbergh, some people called her Lady Lindy.

Eleanor married Franklin Roosevelt, who later became the president of the United States. Over time, Eleanor outgrew her shyness. As first lady, she wrote a newspaper column and even had her own radio show. She used her position to fight **poverty** and **prejudice.** Even after her husband died, Eleanor stayed active in public service.

On April 20, 1933, the two women shared an adventure. That evening, the Roosevelts invited Amelia and her husband to dine at the White House. Before the evening was over, Amelia had invited the first lady to go flying after dinner. Eleanor agreed. No amount of protest by the Secret Service could stop them. Soon, the two women, wearing their **elegant** evening dresses and long white gloves, boarded the plane.

The two regular pilots flew most of the trip. Amelia and Eleanor watched the lights of the city. They spotted the golden glow of the Capitol dome. They saw the Potomac River glistening below. Then the pilots let the women into the **cockpit.** As a trained flier, Amelia took over the controls for a while. Eleanor listened as one of the pilots explained the controls to her. Far below, reporters saw the plane dip slightly. They joked that the first lady must be flying it. The flight was over all too soon, and the two women headed back to the White House. Their adventure made the news.

Eleanor loved the flight and wanted to learn how to pilot a plane herself. She even got a student pilot's license. Amelia had offered to teach her how to fly. President Roosevelt thought flying was too risky, so Eleanor gave up her dream of becoming a pilot. Still, she loved to travel by plane. At that time, flying from one place to another was still a great adventure. Eleanor flew so often that she was given the nickname Eleanor Everywhere.

Amelia wanted to be the first woman to fly around the world. After her first attempt failed, she started again on June 1, 1937. Amelia made it three-fourths of the way. Then she **vanished** without a trace in the Pacific. No one knows what happened to her. Ten ships and 65 planes joined the massive search for Amelia. Nothing was ever found. The mystery of her disappearance has never been solved.

Eleanor and Amelia shared more than an adventure. They shared a friendship and became role models for women. They proved that women could follow their dreams and achieve any goals they set for themselves. Amelia, the little girl who loved flying down snowy hills on her sled, became a famous female pilot. Eleanor, the shy little girl who spent so much time alone, spoke to people all over the world in her fight for human rights. Both women still inspire girls everywhere to fly high in pursuit of their dreams.

Lady Lindy and the First Lady

Activities

1 Vocabulary

Before reading "Lady Lindy and the First Lady," send students on an expedition to discover and use the meanings of new words. Begin by listing the selection's boldfaced words on the chalkboard. Read each word aloud with the class. Invite students to share their prior knowledge of familiar words. (For unknown words, have students locate the definitions using a dictionary.) After discussing each word's meaning, ask a student to make up a sentence using the word. Follow up by having each student complete the activity on page 77 as directed.

2 Drawing Conclusions

Explain to students that an author sometimes conveys a message to his readers without saying it directly. The author gives the reader clues in the form of statements or facts. The reader uses the information along with his own experience and common sense to *draw a conclusion*. Invite a student to read the first paragraph aloud. Point out that the reader might draw the conclusion that Amelia probably didn't play very often with other girls her age since they would have had different interests. Follow up by having each student complete the activity on page 78 as directed.

3 Main Idea and Supporting Details

Focus students' attention on main idea and supporting details with this activity. Point out that Amelia Earhart and Eleanor Roosevelt both made headlines in their day. Ask students to recall several events mentioned in the selection that might have been covered by the newspapers at the time, such as Amelia and Eleanor's flying adventure. Write the responses on the chalkboard. Then have each student choose an event from this list. Instruct her to use details from the selection and her imagination to write a headline and brief news article about the event. Post the news articles on a bulletin board titled "Extra! Extra! Read All About It!"

4 Author's Purpose

Remind students that an author's purpose in writing may be to entertain, persuade, teach, or inform. Use the following questions to help students understand that, in this case, the author's primary purpose was to inform the reader about the lives of two famous women.
- Does the selection try to make us laugh or entertain us?
- Does the selection try to make us agree about a topic?
- Does the selection try to teach us how to do something?
- Does the selection give us facts about a topic?

Finally, have students write an explanation of the author's primary purpose and support it with facts about each of the famous women.

5 Character

Involve students in taking a closer look at the qualities that made Amelia and Eleanor special. Provide each student with a 9" x 12" sheet of construction paper, six 2" x 4" paper strips, scissors, and a length of string. Brainstorm a list of each woman's character traits and record the responses on the chalkboard. Direct each student to write three traits for each woman, each on a separate strip. Then, on the back of each strip, instruct the student to write a detail supporting the trait. Direct each student to cut an airplane shape from the construction paper and label it as shown. Have students hang the strips with string from the appropriate plane section. If desired, suspend the mobiles from the ceiling to remind students of traits that helped make the two women great.

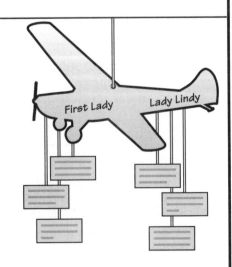

What's for Dessert?

Part 1: Write the letter of each vocabulary word on the line next to its definition. Use a dictionary if you need help.

a. cockpit	1. ____	to dash away suddenly	
b. embroider	2. ____	to disappear	
c. prejudice	3. ____	clumsy, not graceful	
d. bolt	4. ____	an active, athletic girl	
e. elegant	5. ____	a strong feeling or opinion formed unfairly	
f. awkward	6. ____	the space on a plane where the pilot sits	
g. solo	7. ____	without a partner, alone	
h. tomboy	8. ____	lack of money and goods, being poor	
i. vanish	9. ____	rich and fine in quality	
j. poverty	10. ____	to decorate by sewing designs with a needle and thread	

Part 2: Answer each question below by circling the letter in either the yes or no column. Write the circled letters in the matching blanks at the bottom of the page to discover the name of the dessert Eleanor served to Amelia the night they went flying together.

	yes	no
1. Do train conductors ride in the **cockpit?**	1. t	u
2. Would someone **embroider** a pillow to make it look fancy?	2. p	g
3. Is **prejudice** an unfair way of judging another person?	3. s	m
4. Do rabbits **bolt** into their burrows when they are in danger?	4. c	b
5. Would a carpenter wear **elegant** clothes when he is at work?	5. v	i
6. Do **awkward** people usually become great figure skaters?	6. a	d
7. Can a person play a piano **solo** alone?	7. k	w
8. Would a **tomboy** rather play with dolls than play baseball?	8. f	o
9. Did the dinosaurs **vanish** millions of years ago?	9. n	z
10. Do wealthy people have to deal with the problems of **poverty?**	10. s	l

Mrs. Roosevelt served angel food cake with a special topping made of strawberries and whipped cream. It was called

____ ____ ____ ____   ____ ____ ____ ____ ____ ____
  2   5   9   7   4   10   8   1   6   3

Note to the teacher: Use with activity 1 on page 76.

Landing on Conclusions

Part 1: Read the following questions. Choose the best conclusion based on these statements and the information given in the selection. Circle or highlight your answer.

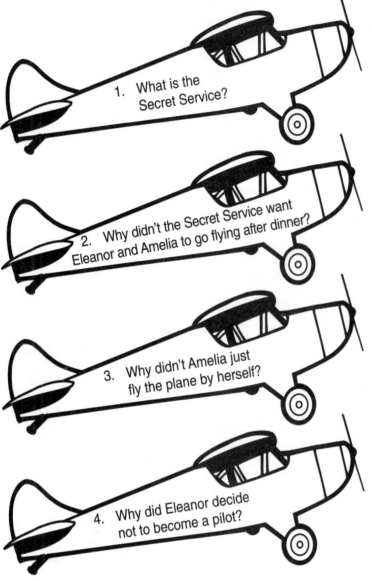

1. What is the Secret Service?

   a. It's a group of people who keep secrets from the president.
   b. No one knows what the Secret Service does.
   c. It's a group of people who protect the president and his family.

2. Why didn't the Secret Service want Eleanor and Amelia to go flying after dinner?

   a. They thought flying was dangerous at night.
   b. They thought flying was too dangerous for the first lady.
   c. They didn't want Amelia and Eleanor to be friends.

3. Why didn't Amelia just fly the plane by herself?

   a. Amelia probably didn't own the plane.
   b. Amelia didn't know how to take off or land the plane.
   c. Amelia and the first lady wanted to look out the windows.

4. Why did Eleanor decide not to become a pilot?

   a. Eleanor was probably too busy doing her radio show and writing for the newspapers.
   b. Eleanor knew the Secret Service didn't want her to fly.
   c. Eleanor's husband probably asked her not to learn to fly.

Part 2: Draw your own conclusions based on the details given below. Write your answers in complete sentences on the lines provided.

1. Riding the roller coaster made Amelia feel as if she were flying. _____
   _____

2. Eleanor used her position as first lady to fight poverty and prejudice. _____
   _____

3. Amelia vanished without a trace over the Pacific Ocean. _____
   _____

4. The United States sent ten ships and 65 planes to search for Amelia. _____
   _____

Answer Keys

Page 5

Part 1

1. fact (baseball)
2. fact (baseball)
3. opinion (cap)
4. fact (baseball)
5. opinion (cap)
6. opinion (cap)
7. fact (baseball)
8. opinion (cap)
9. fact (baseball)
10. opinion (cap)
11. fact (baseball)
12. fact (baseball)

Part 2

Responses will vary.

Page 6

1. Mark enjoyed playing lots of different sports as a boy.
2. On his first time at bat in Little League Baseball, he hit a home run.
3. Mark pitched for his high school baseball team.
4. He hit one ball over a 320-foot fence and another into the next county.
5. Mark was recruited to play baseball for the University of Southern California.
6. While in Alaska, Mark spent hours practicing in the batting cage.
7. After his summer in Alaska, Mark switched to playing first base.
8. Mark began playing for the St. Louis Cardinals in 1998.
9. Mark smashed the record when he hit his 62nd home run.
10. Mark finished the season with 70 home runs.

City on strip: Los Angeles

Page 7

Responses will vary. Possible responses include the following:

A. He could smash the ball and send it soaring out of the park.
   He could smash the ball and send it soaring out of the park and down the hill.
B. He started to cry quietly.
   He started to cry quietly in frustration.
   He started to cry quietly in frustration and hung his head in shame.
   He started to cry quietly in frustration and hung his head in shame as tears ran down his face.
C. The fans in the bleachers screamed.
   The fans in the bleachers screamed loudly.
   The fans in the bleachers screamed loudly and waved their caps in the air.
   The excited fans in the bleachers screamed loudly and waved their caps in the air.

Page 10

1. H
2. G
3. I
4. C
5. E
6. F
7. B
8. J
9. A
10. D

Page 11

Responses may vary. Possible responses include the following:

Competitive—Mia was asked to join the U.S. National Team at an early age. She became the all-time leading scorer in NCAA women's soccer history. She has been named the U.S. Soccer Female Athlete of the Year.
Determined—She kept her promise to stick out every game.
Cooperative—Mia spoke of her team's efforts to reporters.
Caring—She works to help girls succeed in sports.
Encouraging—Mia encourages girls to pursue their goals.
Modest—Mia hasn't let fame go to her head. She spoke of her team's efforts to reporters.

Page 14

1. opinion (yellow)
2. fact (green)
3. opinion (yellow)
4. fact (green)
5. opinion (yellow)
6. opinion (yellow)
7. fact (green)
8. opinion (yellow)
9. fact (green)
10. fact (green)
11. opinion (yellow)
12. fact (green)

Page 15

1. 1950s—Surfers put axles and wheels on wooden boards and "surfed" the streets.
2. 1964—Companies started producing and selling skateboards.
3. 1965—A worldwide competition took place.
4. 1973—The urethane skateboard wheel was invented.
5. 1975—Skateboarders started getting paid and sponsored. Skateboarding became a professional sport.
6. 1977—The first skateboard park was opened.
7. 1978—The ollie was invented by Alan "Ollie" Gelfand.

Page 18

1. stilts
2. review
3. sculptures
4. rare
5. ordinary
6. spunky
7. quest
8. scoured
9. smallpox
10. wanderer

Page 19

Responses will vary. Possible responses include the following:

Part 1

1. She slid down stair railings and slept under the stars. She liked clowns, Ferris wheels, and movies.
2. Her grandfather sometimes paid her a nickel just to sit still for five minutes. Another time, Beverly went to find the pot of gold she'd heard was at the end of a rainbow.
3. She watched cows being milked and sheep being sheared. She teased the chickens and collected their eggs.

Part 2

Responses will vary. Possible responses include the following:

1. The big city was an exciting place.
2. She fell behind because she was absent so much.
3. Ramona seems to have a lot in common with her creator.

Page 23

Responses will vary. Possible responses include the following:

1. "When I was young, I did not study just art, sewing, and music. I learned Latin, math, and astronomy just like my brothers."
2. "I have had family members become ill and die. I tended a dying woman."
3. "I work hard—teaching during the day and studying medical books at night."
4. "I am working as a teacher to earn money for medical school."
5. "A dying woman told me that her suffering would be easier to bear if she had a woman doctor."

Page 24

Responses will vary. Possible answers include the following:

1. e
2. g
3. b
4. h
5. f
6. c
7. a
8. d

Page 27

Responses will vary. Possible responses include the following:

Part 1

1. speaking out, feeling good about playing a sport
2. getting to do the same thing someone else does, being treated fairly
3. hard work, chains
4. guns, fights
5. reading any book I want, having the right to vote
6. anger, mistreating someone

Part 2

1. +
2. +
3. −
4. −
5. +
6. −

Part 3

Responses will vary.

Page 28

Responses will vary. Possible responses include the following:
(Note: Numbers refer to paragraphs in the selection.)

1. Man Mistaken for Scarecrow!
2. Lincoln Communicates Confidence
2./3. Lincoln: Man of Humor
4. Country Sadly Split in Two
5. Southern States Secede
6. Lincoln Takes Charge
7. Lincoln Stands Up for the Union
8. Lincoln Signs Proclamation
9. Former Slaves Join Fight for Freedom
10. Lincoln Killed!

Page 32

Part 1

1. B
2. C
3. D
4. A

Part 2

Responses will vary. Possible responses for 1–3 include the following:

"Its wings of thin, stretchy skin are *open like an umbrella*."
"It is grayish brown, furry, and *as small as a mouse*.
"The hunter moves closer to the cow, *walking on tiptoes like a strange ballet dancer*."
"Its teeth are *as sharp as razors*."

Page 35

a. 5
b. 2
c. 7
d. 6
e. 3
f. 8
g. 4
h. 1

Page 36

1. Komodo dragon
2. crocodile
3. tuatara
4. coelacanth
5. pterosaur
6. mokele-mbembe
7. coelacanth
8. crocodile
9. Komodo dragon
10. mokele-mbembe
11. tuatara
12. pterosaur

Page 39

Analogy	Explanation
1. grass	Jellyfish eat plankton, and cows eat grass.
2. run	Jellyfish move by floating, and cheetahs move by running.
3. umbrella	Jellyfish are shaped like umbrellas, and starfish are shaped like stars.
4. bite	Jellyfish sting their victims, and cobras bite their victims.
5. vertebrate	Jellyfish are invertebrates, and humans are vertebrates.
6. ocean	Jellyfish live in the ocean, and monkeys live in the jungle.
7. arms	Jellyfish have many tentacles, and octopuses have many arms.
8. sensor	Jellyfish use sensors to get information, and insects use antennae to get information.
9. snake	Jellyfish are a type of zooplankton, and snakes are a type of reptile.
10. fly	Jellyfish are eaten by leatherback sea turtles, and flies are eaten by spiders.

Page 40

1. opinion (purple)
2. fact (blue)
3. fact (blue)
4. opinion (purple)
5. fact (blue)
6. opinion (purple)
7. fact (blue)
8. opinion (purple)
9. fact (blue)
10. fact (blue)

Page 43

Will-o'-the-Wisps
4, 7, 10, 12
Ball Lightning
1, 3, 5, 9
Ghost Lights
2, 6, 8, 11

Page 44
1. opinion
2. fact
3. opinion
4. fact
5. fact
6. opinion
7. fact
8. opinion
9. opinion
10. fact

Page 47
1
Air moves as it warms or cools.
Much of the weather on Earth is affected by the wind.
2
Certain winds seem to carry sickness.
Some people seem to get tense or upset.
3
The winds blast hot, dry air into the Los Angeles area.
They can spark fires that can be seen from space.
4
It blows across the Mediterranean Sea, picking up moisture as it moves along.
This wind blows rain and fog into Europe.
5
When the wind spirals down from the mountains, it moves faster.
It can reach speeds of up to 60 mph and can damage crops.
6
Positive ions from these winds can give people headaches, pains, and chills.
People have reported trouble sleeping.

Page 48
1. blanket
2. kite
3. race car
4. football field
5. poison
6. wolf
7. ice
8. funnel
9. toys

Page 51
Part 1
1. Responses will vary. 2003 (as of date of publication)
2. Responses will vary. 2003 – 1972 = 31 years (as of date of publication)
3. 1931
4. 50 medicine wheels
5. 44 medicine wheels
6. 70 feet
7. 28 spokes
8. 1,008 feet
9. 500 years
Part 2
IT'S IN WYOMING

Page 52
1. early
2. sunrise
3. damp
4. summit
5. secret
6. circular
7. spoke
8. shaman
9. powerful
10. astronomer
11. calendar
12. lowest
13. rising
14. seasons
15. ancient
16. harvest

Page 55
1. forest
2. global
3. sound
4. vivid
5. unbelievable
6. back
7. rock
8. light
9. book
10. ocean
11. scared
12. sky
13. worry
14. slow
15. dog

Page 56
Responses may vary. Possible responses include the following:
1. Tremors Felt by Sunbathers on Kiwya's Beaches
2. Kiwya Spits Smoke and Ash—Is Trouble Brewing?
3. Frightened Tourists Flee Smoky Paradise
4. Government Orders Evacuation of Kiwya Islanders
5. Islanders Evacuated As Kiwya Spews More Ash
6. Kiwya Explodes! Island Buried in Ash
7. Tsunami Damage Evaluated
8. Tokyo Wonders, "Is Our City on Fire?"
9. Global Temperatures Drop Months After Kiwya Blast
10. Scientists Return to Kiwya to Study Volcano's Impact

Page 57
Part 1
The sleeping volcano had turned into a fire-breathing dragon. The volcano was fiery and dangerous.
Part 2
Responses will vary.

Page 60
1. extraterrestrial
2. meteorite
3. astronomer
4. circular
5. unidentified
6. ufologist
7. emerged
8. television
9. encounter
10. writhing

Page 65
1. True—D
2. False—O
3. False—I
4. True—A
5. True—N
6. False—S
7. True—E
8. False—M
9. True—S
10. True—A
11. False—N
12. False—N
13. False—U
14. True—T
Cool Connection: Andes Mountains

Page 68
1. rouse
2. distress
3. starboard
4. bow
5. steward
6. crow's nest
7. hull
8. gymnasium
9. horizon
10. stern

Page 69
Responses will vary. Possible responses include the following:
1. Two men in the crow's nest looked for icebergs ahead of the ship.
$3.00 + ($.35 \times 3) = $4.05
2. It was already too late to slow and turn the ship when the orders were given by the First Officer.
$3.00 + ($.35 \times 10) = $6.50
3. Freezing water flooded six sections of *Titanic's* double-bottom hull.
$3.00 + ($.35 \times 0) = $3.00
4. *Titanic's* builders didn't put enough lifeboats on the ship for all of its passengers.
$3.00 + ($.35 \times 4) = $4.40
5. When the front of the ship dipped into the water, people left behind may have fled toward the back.
$3.00 + ($.35 \times 9) = $6.15
6. The shivering people in the lifeboats watched helplessly as *Titanic* sank.
$3.00 + ($.35 \times 1) = $3.35

Page 70

CALIFORNIAN

Page 73
Part 1
1. eel
   red ★
2. bay
   red ★
3. hurricane
   red ▲
4. forecasters
   red ▲
5. informed
   purple ●
6. squalls
   red ★
7. yachting
   purple ●
8. spared
   purple ★
9. survive
   purple ●
10. toppled
    purple ●
11. plowed
    purple ★
12. detour
    red ●
Part 2
Responses will vary.

Page 74
1. A flock of birds is acting goofy.
2. It is a gray, rainy day.
3. Skating is canceled because part of the roof has blown off.
4. A power line breaks and swings in the wind.
5. The roof of the hardware store rips off.
6. The ocean plows through the West Bay Bathing Club.
7. They drive through pounding wind, and past falling trees and rushing water.
8. Arthur thinks about his grandfather out on the bay in his small fishing boat.
9. Arthur desperately wants to get home.
10. Arthur rushes into the house.

Page 77
Part 1
1. d
2. i
3. f
4. h
5. c
6. a
7. g
8. j
9. e
10. b
Part 2
1. no (u)
2. yes (p)
3. yes (s)
4. yes (c)
5. no (i)
6. no (d)
7. yes (k)
8. no (o)
9. yes (n)
10. no (l)
Puzzle: pink clouds

Page 78
Part 1
1. c
2. b
3. a
4. c
Part 2
Responses will vary. Possible responses include the following:
1. It made Amelia want to try flying a real plane someday.
2. Eleanor was able to express her ideas on radio, in newspapers, and to important people she met because she was the president's wife.
3. Amelia's plane probably crashed into the ocean and sank.
4. Amelia was an important American hero who inspired people with her courage.